GW00579689

The Staff Corps

The History of the Engineer and
Logistic Staff Corps RE

This unit was formerly known as
the Engineer and Railway Staff Corps RE

and for a short time as
the Engineer and Transport Staff Corps RE

The badges opposite are those of the Royal Engineers,
left, and the Royal Logistic Corps, the two Corps
which the Staff Corps serves.

The Staff Corps

*The History of the Engineer and
Logistic Staff Corps RE*

Major General G B Sinclair, CB, CBE

Front cover:
Sleigh Post by Terence Cuneo (1907–1996) showing
men of the Postal Branch of the Royal Engineers
trans-shipping mail from rail to sleighs for
distribution to British troops in North Russia in 1919.

Back cover:
Three operations to which the Staff Corps
contributed advice and expertise.

Top: Bridge layer crews preparing for battle during
the 1990 Gulf War (see Chapter Eight).

Centre: Dynamic compaction trial to develop the
Royal Engineers capability for Airfield Damage
Repair (see Chapter Five).

Bottom: DROPS vehicle of the Royal Logistics Corps
(see Chapter Seven).

First published in Great Britain 2001 by
Royal Engineers Museum
Brompton Barracks, Chatham ME4 4UG

Copyright © 2001 G B Sinclair

G B Sinclair has asserted his moral right to be identified as author of this work.

A catalogue record for this book is available from the British Library.

ISBN 0-9506453-9-7

Project management: Christopher Pick (020 8761 2585)
Book design: Adam Hay (020 7628 3737)

Printed and bound by Technographic Design and Print Ltd.

Contents

Preface

This short history was written to enable newly joined officers of the Engineer and Logistic Staff Corps RE(V) and members of the Armed Services encountering it for the first time to understand something of its past and what it does now. The late Major C E C Townsend, of the Staff Corps, wrote a very detailed study, entitled *All Rank and No File*, together with a Supplement, relating what went on inside the Staff Corps until 1980. This is an excellent source of information for the early years and I have drawn upon it greatly. I have tried to put the major events described in the political and military context of the time to make more clear the use to which the country and the Armed Services put the Staff Corps.

'All Rank and No File' is an accurate description of the organisation, because since its foundation as the Engineer and Railway Staff Corps right up to today it has never had any soldiers, only officers. It is a body of highly experienced and qualified people, at the top of their professions, who become TA officers so as to give advice on matters of engineering and logistics. They receive no pay, do no military training, perform no military duties, do not carry military identity cards and, except on very rare occasions, are not allowed to wear military uniform. The Army gets them for the price of a very small capitation grant each year, and the members themselves have to pay an enrolment fee and an annual subscription.

Although in the early days the Staff Corps had no relationship with the Corps of Royal Engineers, later it did become part of that Corps. When the branches of the Royal Engineers that dealt with transport and movements were transferred to the newly formed Royal Corps of Transport, the Staff Corps found itself serving two 'cap-badge' Corps of the Regular Army. The Royal Corps of Transport itself was later absorbed into the newly formed Royal Logistic Corps. This means that in recent years there are a confusing number of Corps in this story, so I have always referred to our subject as the Staff Corps to distinguish it from the many other Corps.

When referring to personalities I have used the name and rank that they had at the time of the event.

I wish to express my gratitude to General Sir Charles Guthrie, Chief of the Defence Staff, for writing the Foreword. I also acknowledge with thanks the great assistance and support I have had from Colonel John Taberner, the former Acting Adjutant and now Honorary Treasurer of the Staff Corps, in preparing this book and checking the proofs.

G B Sinclair
St Boswells, Roxburghshire
February 2001

General Sir Charles Guthrie, GCB, LVO, OBE, Chief of the Defence Staff, 1997–2001.

Foreword

The Engineer and Railway Staff Corps (as it was originally known) was a uniquely British solution to a military problem. Its continued existence, today as the Engineer and Logistic Staff Corps, is a great credit to the very many highly professional civilians who volunteered to join it and also to the flexibility of the British Army which allowed it to adapt to changing circumstances and requirements.

The Staff Corps is a remarkable body of some of the best brains and most able managers in British industry. It is highly commendable that such busy people give so much of their time willingly and without reward to make an effective and practical contribution to the national defence effort.

As the Armed Forces are asked to take on new tasks, or familiar tasks in unfamiliar territory, and the pressure on military manpower and budgets remains high, the need for such a body as the Engineer and Logistic Staff Corps only increases.

This is a fitting time for this history to appear as the country enters a period when very few have first-hand knowledge of the Armed Services. In only two or three years there will be no one left in business or industry who did National Service. It was fortunate that the Staff Corps persuaded Gus Sinclair, a previous Honorary Colonel of the Corps and a former Engineer-in-Chief of the Army, to write this history. It needs to be known.

General Sir Charles Guthrie
Chief of the Defence Staff
London, February 2001

9

Chapter One

Origins

After the Treaty of Paris in 1856, imposed on the Russians by the victorious allies at the conclusion of the Crimean War, the brief period of amicable Anglo-French relations ended and the mutual distrust and suspicion of former years returned.

In August 1858 Queen Victoria and Prince Albert joined the Emperor Napoleon III and his Empress for a week-long festival at Cherbourg to celebrate the opening of the enlarged port there. The development of this port and the opening of a new rail link from Paris to Cherbourg caused particular unease in Britain. Despite the declarations of continuing friendship by leading personalities, the many Members of Parliament and other notables who attended the festivities were seriously concerned by the new port only 70 miles across the Channel from Britain. On 9 August *The Times*'s correspondent reported that there were 'cannons, cannons, cannons, wherever you turned. They poured from every corner, they commanded every turning. One could not help wondering what in the name of wonder they were meant to attack or defend.'

Questions of defence dominated Britain for most of 1859. The Institution of Civil Engineers spent five evenings discussing a paper on the national defences. On 12 May the Government formally approved the re-creation of the Volunteer movement; the original Volunteers had been disbanded in 1814 after the threat of French invasion had passed. When Lord Palmerston's Liberal Government took office in June 1859, it implemented the re-formation of the Volunteers, who were controlled by the Lord Lieutenant of each county. In August the Government also set up a Royal Commission on National Defence and created, for the first time, a Royal Navy Volunteer Reserve.

The response to the re-formation of the Volunteers was enthusiastic. Recruits poured in throughout the country, despite having to pay a subscription to join. The previous Volunteers had had to march around the country. Now Britain was criss-crossed by railways able to transport men and equipment rapidly. However the railways were owned by almost 100 different companies, each competing for traffic and reluctant to co-operate with one another. No one knew how they were likely to respond in the national interest in the event of a need to mobilise. This did not augur well for the kind of collaboration that would be necessary to move the Volunteers and the Regular Army as rapidly as possible in times of emergency.

The creation of the Engineer and Railway Staff Corps largely resulted from the initiative of one man, Charles Manby, Honorary Secretary of the Institution of Civil Engineers. Charles Manby was the eldest son of Aaron Manby, founder of Horseley Engineering and Ironworks, a few miles from Birmingham. He was born on 4 February 1804 and was sent at the early age of ten to a semi-military college in Brittany. It was said that soon afterwards he obtained a commission in the British Army, held for only a short time, through the influence of his uncle Captain Joseph Manby, who was ADC and Private Secretary to the Duke of Kent.

At the end of the Napoleonic Wars, Manby returned home to study engineering at his father's works. In 1822 he installed and worked the engines of the *Manby*, the first steamship built on the Thames, and the following year he went to Paris to work in his father's new factory at Charenton. He installed gas lighting in the streets of Paris and reorganised the famous Creuzot Works before returning to England in 1829. After spending a few years managing an ironworks in South Wales, Manby settled in London in 1835, where he introduced an early form of central heating.

In 1839 Manby became the first paid Secretary of the Institution of Civil Engineers, which was at that time languishing under the uninspired leadership of James Walker, its second President. Walker imagined that, like his great predecessor Thomas Telford, he could hold his appointment until he died. Manby infused fresh life into the Institution, drafted a new constitution which included a clause limiting each President's term of office to two years, and greatly increased the number of members. When he resigned his post in 1856 in order to return to private practice he was elected Honorary Secretary, an appointment he held until his death 28 years later.

Lieutenant Colonel Charles Manby, founder of the Staff Corps and Acting Adjutant 1865–1884, in full dress uniform of the day.

Manby had many interests. He was very active in promoting the Great Exhibition of 1851 and the Suez Canal Company, and for many years he also managed the Adelphi and Haymarket Theatres. As the London and Overseas Representative of Messrs G R Stephenson and Company, he was well acquainted with the managements of many railways both at home and abroad and did much to encourage foreign railways to develop using British engineering skills and capital. In return for these services he was frequently honoured by foreign governments; in the portrait on page 13 he wears the breast star and collar badge of the Swedish Order of Wasa, the breast star and decoration of the Brazilian Order of the Rose, the Italian decoration of the Order of St Maurice and St Lazarus, and the badge of the French Légion d'Honneur as well as other decorations that cannot be identified.

On 2 July 1860 Manby wrote to members of the Institution's Council proposing the formation of a 'Volunteer Engineering Staff Corps for the Arrangement of the Transport of Troops and Stores, the Construction of defensive works and the destruction of other works, in case of Invasion' and asking them to attend a Council meeting to discuss the idea.

In August that year Manby produced a memorandum proposing to use Officers of a new 'Volunteer Corps of Engineers' to organise the railways into large working groups when war threatened. Each group would come under the command of a member of the Institution's Council; officers of this new Volunteer Corps drawn from the railways would serve under them. His scheme was submitted to the War Office through the Lord Lieutenant of the County of Middlesex. Sydney Herbert, the Secretary of State for War, responded that he highly appreciated the public spirit of the Institution and that the formation of such a Corps would be 'a great advantage to the Public Service'. As this Corps would be so novel, he asked that a small committee of members of the Institution's Council and officers from the War Office be formed to consider the proposal fully.

Despite the War Office's encouragement, the railway companies refused to admit either the necessity for or the advantages of the proposed system; Manby also met some opposition from the Council of the Institution. Not until September 1864 was he able to write to the War Office to report that he had agreement from some 20 people interested in forming a Corps.

Manby's original proposal for the Staff Corps was now approved. Colonel W M S McMurdo, the Inspector General of Volunteers, wrote that 'it was hoped that… the extreme importance of the Corps would become understood and its utility developed.' He also redefined the original aim of the Corps in the following words:

> 1st. To secure unity of action throughout the Railway system of the United Kingdom in time of invasion to the end that troops and material may be transported in any required direction with certainty and the utmost rapidity.
> 2nd. That works of construction and destruction in connection with railway communications which the exigencies of war may render necessary should be carried out with equal certainty and rapidity.

He went on to say that one of the principal duties of the Corps would be the preparation in peacetime of schemes for the movement and concentration of troops in the shortest possible time.

It was suggested that initially the Corps should be limited to three classes of members:

> *Lieutenant Colonels* to include the leading Civil Engineers of the country who are, or have been, connected with the construction of the Main Lines, and the General Managers of the Main and Mail Lines of Railways.
> *Majors* to include Locomotive and Resident Engineers of the Main and Mail Lines, some of the Higher Class of Contractors and Secretaries of Lines who are also General Managers.
> *Captains* to include Traffic Managers of Main Lines, General Managers of Branch Lines and Civil Engineers attached to Branch Lines.

Her Majesty the Queen accepted the services of the Engineer and Railway Staff Corps on 4 January 1865. Shortly afterwards the commissions of twelve civil engineers and nine general managers as Lieutenant Colonels were gazetted as the first officers of the Staff Corps. G P Bidder, a Past President of the Institution of Civil Engineers, was appointed Lieutenant Colonel Commandant and remained in command until his death in September 1878, a span of over thirteen years.

Manby was appointed the first Acting Adjutant of the Staff Corps in the same month. He was given the title Acting Adjutant because the normal rank of an

Adjutant in the Army was (and remains) Captain, whereas Manby was to serve as a Lieutenant Colonel. The title has continued in the Staff Corps to this day for the same reason, although in recent times it has been filled by either a Lieutenant Colonel or a Colonel. The Acting Adjutant combined two roles; he served as Secretary/Treasurer of the Staff Corps and also as the Executive Officer of the Council of Colonels, which consists of senior members of the Staff Corps and acts as its ruling body.

Manby's health started to deteriorate after about eight years, but he would not allow anyone to relieve him of his duties. Consequently the Corps records, except for the Exercises described in Chapter Two, became very scanty. He died on 31 July 1884 at Eastbourne, aged 80, theoretically still in post.

George Parker Bidder, the first Commandant of the Staff Corps 1865–1878.

The Exercises

Shortly after the Staff Corps was founded it embarked on the first of five successive Exercises, which occupied the years between 1865 and 1885. Ordered and set by the War Office, these Exercises were designed to plan for moving and concentrating troops in the event of an invasion and represented the only planning undertaken for this eventuality.

At the first meeting of the Council of the Staff Corps, on 3 April 1865, Colonel W M S McMurdo, who had been appointed the first Honorary Colonel, presented an exercise setting. This involved moving an army of 280,000 men of all arms, Regulars, Militia and Volunteers, from all over Great Britain into a concentration area to forestall an invasion.

During May the Exercise was circulated in print to all Staff Corps members. It stated that the country was at war with two maritime powers; naval engagements had been indecisive; a naval force had been despatched to the north to counter an enemy fleet, leaving the North Sea coast undefended. It was now necessary to throw the land forces into strategic positions to repel any attempt at invasion between the Thames and the Wash.

The Staff Corps now divided into its two disciplines. The Railway component was asked to work out the movements of men, horses and guns from all parts of England, Wales and Scotland to the deployment areas. (Ireland was not covered by the Volunteer Act and so was outside the scope of operations of the Corps.) This required the movement of 155,684 men, 22,900 horses and 260 guns to the main concentration area between Colchester and March; 48,111 men and 78 guns to the reserve area in Bedfordshire; 31,391 men, 850 horses and 62 guns to reinforce the garrisons in Kent; and over 20,000 men each to Portsmouth and Plymouth to stiffen the defences. The movements were to be arranged 'with the utmost rapidity and certainty and special consideration was to be given to maintaining the supply of food for the population of London and other large towns which were wholly dependent on the railways for their daily supply.'

The Engineers meanwhile were asked to consider the creation of obstacles, including inundation and the strengthening of natural lines of defence, in three possible areas of operations: between the Thames and Colchester; between Colchester and Lowestoft; and between Lowestoft and the Wash.

So many novel problems of railway operation were involved that it was decided to set up nine sub-committees, each consisting of the General Manager of the principal railway in the area together with his geographical neighbours.

It took about one year to work out all the problems and co-ordinate the answer. The *Answer to Exercise One*, presented to General Sir John Burgoyne, the Inspector General of Fortifications, on 30 November 1866, was a printed document of 20 pages, to which was attached a 'Rolling Stock Return' and massive and detailed timetables for every train movement. Copies of the Return and the timetables no longer exist, but it is known that the movement to East Anglia required 962 trains, which were expected to average 25 mph, and that the total time required from receipt of the order-to-move until the last train arrived was 80 hours.

The reports of the Engineers on this and on nearly all the later Exercises were not permitted to be printed, and no manuscript copy appears to have been kept by the Staff Corps.

There is an interesting footnote to the conduct of Exercise One. General Burgoyne carried out the Annual Inspection in the middle of the work on the Exercise. Afterwards he wrote to the Acting Adjutant that:

> It is evident that every Memoir and Paper, presented to the Council by the Members, must have required much labour not only from the officer himself but his assistants – draughtsmen, clerks etc., and that many were also the occasion for considerable other expense, such as for Travelling, Books, Maps and other matters: Is all this at the charge of the individual officer who undertakes the work or is there any fund to contribute towards it?

General (later Field Marshal) Sir John Burgoyne, who did much to encourage the Staff Corps in its early days.

Manby answered that that the individual officers and the sub-committees bore all the expenses connected with the Exercise. As a result General Burgoyne organised for an annual Capitation Grant to be paid to the Corps, as it was to other Volunteer units.

A year after Exercise One was presented, Major General McMurdo (as he now was) tabled an introductory memorandum for Exercise Two for discussion at the 1867 Annual Inspection, which was again conducted by General Burgoyne. Printed copies of the setting, when agreed, were distributed, and meetings of both Railway and Engineer groups took place on 20 April 1868. The setting assumed

General Sir William McMurdo: as Inspector General of Volunteers, while still a Colonel, he played an important role in the formation of the Staff Corps and subsequently served as its first Honorary Colonel.

that no sooner had the troop movements for Exercise One been completed than it was discovered that the threat to East Anglia was a feint and the real invasion was to take place between Hengistbury Head, south of Christchurch, and Bournemouth.

The Railway group had to move the troops from East Anglia to the Romsey-Southampton area. When they had completed the task, they found it would require 692 trains, 531 of which would have to pass through Basingstoke at five-minute intervals!

The task assigned to the Engineer group proved much more difficult and lasted much longer. The Engineers were instructed to consider how to prevent an enemy force landing in Bridgwater Bay from:
1 advancing by rail to Salisbury, Wimborne and Dorchester to link up with the main invading force;
2 moving towards Devonport;
3 capturing the unfortified city of Bristol.

The Engineers spent several days reconnoitring the ground in Hampshire and Somerset, but found that to solve the problem they needed to know much more about the Army. It was impossible to design a defensive position without understanding the Army's preferences and requirements for temporary earthworks and siting temporary gun positions, the state of training of the troops involved, and many other details. They also asked if they could attend experiments and practical operations at Chatham, the School and training base of the Royal Engineers, and at Shoeburyness, where artillery training and experiments were carried out.

At the next Annual Inspection on 28 November 1868, the Commandant of the Corps reported to the Inspecting Officer, Major General E Frome, the Director of Works in the War Office, that the Engineers could not complete their part of the Exercise for lack of information and co-operation. Lack of co-operation between the regular Royal Engineers and the Engineer and Railway Staff Corps persisted for years, and at this time there were no links, formal or informal, between the two Corps. The difficulties were reported to Major General Sir William Gordon, the Inspector General of Royal Engineers, in November 1869, and were repeated to Major General Sir F P Haines, the Quartermaster General (QMG), when he made the Annual Inspection in November 1870. There is now no evidence of the cause of this problem, but it does appear that the War Office was just as culpable as the Royal Engineers, if not more so. Although the Exercise was conducted for the War Office, the QMG, the Director of Works and the Inspector General RE had all failed to remove the blockage.

Exercise Three, sent by the War Office to the Staff Corps early in 1872, envisaged an enemy landing on the south coast between Hastings and Brighton and marching on London. One is entitled to ask how much this Exercise was inspired by the fearful prospect of a German invasion of Britain, as described in Colonel George Chesney's book *The Battle of Dorking*, published in Edinburgh in 1871. Although a work of fiction, the book was widely read and made a large impact throughout Britain, leading commentators to question whether the British Army was capable of resisting an enemy invasion or fighting a major war.

The Railway group was asked to plan for bringing reservists to Redhill. The Engineer group was asked to consider the demolition of roads, bridges and railways in order to impede the enemy's advance towards Redhill, where the defending forces would make a stand. It was also required to consider the construction of an entrenched position, complete with redoubts and abattis, to prevent an advance on the high roads passing through Reigate, Redhill and Godstone.

At last, not only had the Engineer component been asked to advise on specific questions, but the War Office decided that a Royal Engineers officer should accompany Staff Corps officers when they made their reconnaissance on the ground and afford them all assistance in military matters.

Although this was not stated in so many words, the Engineers of the Staff Corps rejected the War Office's setting. They ruled out an enemy landing east of Hastings: 'this must be an impossible area otherwise why should the numerous Martello Towers have been demolished so recently?' The Group also considered that there was insufficient space for a large-scale landing at Seaford and Newhaven and concluded that the most likely landing place was to the west of Brighton, from where the enemy would advance on Horsham via the Adur valley.

On the subject of demolition, the Engineers stated that within the previous three years much practical knowledge had been gained in using explosives for defence purposes and recommended that guncotton should be used against bridges, tunnels and large buildings. They calculated that the earthwork defences for the 113 guns would involve shifting 11,000 cubic yards of earth and could be completed by a force of 2,000 navvies in 48 hours. The Majors, all of whom were contractors, said that they could provide this force and get the job done within three days of the alarm being raised. Moreover the Engineer group stated that it would arrange to transport and feed the men (perhaps, knowing their gargantuan appetites, the Majors feared for their efficiency if they were fed by the Army).

The Engineers also expressed concern that the Exercise stipulated that the defensive measures, including the building of obstructions, were to be taken 'after the main body of the defensive force had fallen back'. Placing a large group of navvies between two armies, they pointed out, could only create confusion on the line of retreat. Nor was the Staff Corps, let alone civilian contractors, intended to be employed in operations in front of the enemy.

Although the answers to the Engineering Questions in Exercise Three were printed – the only ones ever published in this way – they were not dated. It was probably 1873 before they were delivered, after which three years passed before the next Exercise.

Exercise Four came from the War Office in May 1876, and differed radically from the three previous ones. The shock of the Franco-Prussian War and the brilliant reforms introduced by Edward Cardwell, Gladstone's Secretary of State for War from 1868 to 1874, were beginning to have an effect. New ideas on mobilisation had been promulgated and the Army at home was to be organised into Corps, Divisions and Brigades, each of which would be despatched as an entity to its allotted defensive position.

In the three previous Exercises the Staff Corps had been instructed to assemble troops *en masse* at the rendezvous. For this new Exercise an invasion of the north-east coast of Norfolk was to be met by putting I Army Corps around Norwich and II, III and V Army Corps in front of Bury St Edmunds, with VI and VII Army Corps forming a second line of defence in the rear. The requirement was to move 177,815 men, 61,366 horses and 540 guns.

Discussion of the Exercise lasted for four years, and the answer was not sent to the War Office until April 1880. As electric block signalling was by then in general use, trains would be separated by space rather than by a time interval. While the loading and despatch of the special trains did not involve any problems, the disembarkation at points of concentration presented considerable difficulty. Reference was made to trials held in July 1873, when three Regiments of Cavalry were carried by rail from Aldershot to Exeter; four trains of 30 vehicles each were required for each Regiment, and it was found that 30 minutes between trains was ample for loading and detraining.

Staff Corps officers had clearly had enough of requests to prepare detailed timetables, and said:

> Such cannot be necessary, or if made would not be of any practical use…
> Elaborate Timetables were prepared and printed for Exercise One; the
> Answers to Exercise Two and Three gave full details of the time required
> by trains and of the requisite rolling stock. Any new detailed statement…
> could for the fourth time repeat the information already supplied by the
> Corps, at great labour and expense, without giving any new result or
> in any way altering the principles upon which the tables already supplied
> were framed.

In essence Exercise Five, put before the Staff Corps in June 1882, was the same problem posed 17 years earlier, i.e. opposition to an enemy landing between

Shoeburyness and Southend. Six Army Corps had to be moved into defensive positions around Basildon within 48 hours, involving 151,791 men, 39,643 horses and 3,931 vehicles. It is not apparent what Engineer questions the War Office posed and, as they were not allowed to be printed, we shall never know what the Engineers contributed.

So ended the five Exercises carried out for the War Office. Each, together with its answer, was printed on good-quality foolscap paper; the printed timetable of 1865 contained 311 octavo pages. The total cost of production was £1,176, 18 shillings and 6 pence, about £15,000 at today's prices. This cost was born entirely by the funds of the Staff Corps, without subsidy from the War Office.

The February 1885 issue of the popular monthly review *The Nineteenth Century* included an article by a retired General, Sir Edward Hamley, entitled 'The Volunteers in Time of Need'. In it he argued that likely areas for hostile landings in Britain should be reconnoitred and detailed plans prepared to meet an invasion. He called for the movement of troops to be worked out in advance, down to the exact use of every item of road and rail transport. It is clear from his article that Hamley had some knowledge of the Staff Corps, albeit inaccurate, and he cast doubt on the competence of the Staff Corps to undertake such planning because they were civil engineers and not railway men.

The April issue of *The Nineteenth Century* contained a riposte that firmly put Sir Edward right about the Staff Corps and its members. The article, entitled 'In Case of Invasion', was by Archibald Forbes, a distinguished war correspondent of the *Daily News*, and in it he described in great detail the problems addressed in Exercises One, Three and Five. Exercise Five had only been delivered to the War Office two months earlier. The War Office was most upset by Forbes' article, and the Assistant Quartermaster General wrote to the Commandant, Lieutenant Colonel Sir John Hawkshaw, requiring an explanation as to how Mr Forbes had gained access to the work that had gone into the Exercises. After an investigation the Commandant replied that no officer of his Corps had any knowledge of how Archibald Forbes had obtained his information. Strangely the matter ended there. Perhaps it is too fanciful to imagine that somebody realised that, by countering unfounded and unjustified public criticism of the War Office by an uninformed retired General, Forbes' article might just give the public confidence in its preparations for war.

Chapter Three

Organising Railways for War

The formation and development of the Staff Corps was a typically British solution, based on improvisation and pragmatism, to a problem addressed in a totally different way on the continent of Europe.

Prussia was acutely aware of the military importance of railways and much of its rail network was built with strategic considerations in mind. In 1858 Count Helmuth von Moltke had become the Chief of the Prussian General Staff and had set about making it a model of efficiency. The department of the General Staff responsible for mobilisation was also responsible for the efficient functioning of the railways in war and the plans for the deployment of the Army. Von Moltke put theory into practice in the Seven Weeks War against Austria in 1866, during which the Prussian General Staff made remarkable use of the railways as an aid to strategic concentration. However, von Moltke was not totally satisfied with the co-ordination of the movement of troops and supplies by rail, and immediately took steps to correct the few failings.

The railways of the United Kingdom were created in complete commercial freedom. By contrast, all the continental systems were conterminous and in their development and operation had to meet military requirements. A large part of the European network was state-owned, and with varying degrees of success all the continental powers devised systems to regulate and control their entire wagon stock.

In the 1860s France constructed strategic rail lines and also attempted to rebuild, train and re-equip a large Army. The one crucial area the French ignored was the formation of an efficient General Staff. Their organisation for

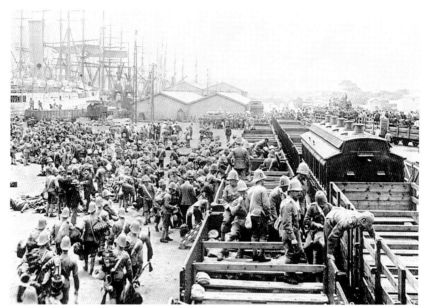

The Second Battalion Royal Fusiliers entraining at Durban in 1899. Entraining and detraining facilities, including temporary ones, were major factors in the Exercises.

mobilisation and deployment, and for the movement of troops and supplies by rail, was minimal. When put to the test by the Franco-Prussian War of 1870 it failed completely.

By 1890 all the major continental armies had adopted a General Staff system modelled on the Prussian/German Army, and every continental nation had a system for controlling railways in war. Despite widespread fears of invasion the UK refused to address either the General Staff or the railway problems until much later.

As we have seen in Chapter Two, the five Exercises the Staff Corps carried out between 1865 and 1885 represented the sole planning undertaken for the movement and concentration of troops in the event of an invasion. In autumn 1870, shortly after the end of the second Exercise, the Quartermaster General, Major General Sir F P Haines, discussed with members of the Staff Corps how the railway could be controlled and directed in time of war. It was considered that appointing a standing council of officers of the Staff Corps might cause difficulties with those railway companies not represented in the Staff Corps. It was therefore proposed that in an emergency the War Office should inform the Acting Adjutant of the Staff Corps of the nature of the movement and the numbers involved; he would then summon the representatives of the railways concerned to arrange the details. It was also recommended that all rolling stock should be at the disposal of the Government and be available to run over any lines of the appropriate gauge; the compensation paid to the railway companies would be settled afterwards.

There the matter rested until 1876 when, in setting the fourth Exercise for the Staff Corps, the War Office warned that 'unless the Military and Railway Authorities cordially co-operated with each other, and the latter among themselves, there would be a great risk that the operation might fail or at any rate be retarded.' Requested by the War Office to consider how best to establish 'perfect relations' between the military and railway authorities, the Staff Corps replied that it had been asked the same question in 1870 and that its answer remained the same. This was that 'some central and responsible authority should be created to permit the various companies to represent their views as to the best mode of conducting the operations.'

The 1871 Regulation of the Forces Act had already given the Government powers to take control of the rail network in an emergency. The Government would nominate persons to take possession and operate the railways; all railway directors and employees were required to obey them. It is almost certain that the War Office did not consult the Staff Corps when the Act was drafted. It was generally felt that the Act's powers were too formidable and that bringing in inexperienced people to control the railways, to the exclusion of the professional management, would only cause chaos.

In 1888 the National Defence Act stated that, whenever the Militia was called out, the Secretary of State could order that military and naval traffic should take precedence over all other rail traffic. Again it seems that the Staff Corps was not consulted about this. Although it was generally believed that these powers superseded those of the 1871 Act, the latter was not repealed.

The Council of the Staff Corps circulated copies of the Act to railway general managers, who were asked to form a committee to study the Act and to report back. As a result the Council asked the War Office to meet a deputation, and in February 1889 it was agreed that the Staff Corps should draw up a Code of Regulation for placing the railways under military control.

In July 1889 Lieutenant Colonel Sir George Findlay, General Manager of the London & North Western Railway, and others produced a memorandum entitled

Organisation of Railway Transport in Time of War. However, his scheme did not meet with the approval of the Honorary Colonel, General Sir William McMurdo. McMurdo had always argued that in time of war the Council of the Staff Corps, 'composed as it is of eminent, experienced and practical persons connected with engineering and railways', should sit '*en permanence*' at the War Office.

Findlay produced another draft, which the Council considered at two meetings. Eventually a modified scheme was sent to the War Office in December 1889. It opened with a clear statement of the case for involvement of the Staff Corps:

> The Engineer and Railway Volunteer Staff Corps being constituted for
> the purposes of directing the application of skilled labour, and of railway
> transport, to the purposes of National Defence, and for preparing in
> time of peace a system on which such duties should be conducted... .

The Memorandum went into some detail about how this would be achieved. Its most important point, however, appeared in its first principle, that in time of war 'the Council, or a section of it, should sit *en permanence* at the War Office.'

The War Office did not take any action to implement the Council's recommendations until 1896. Then the Commandant, Lieutenant Colonel Sir John Fowler, and several officers were summoned to a conference at which it was decided to set up a committee to report on 'The Regulation and Control of Railway Transport on Mobilisation'. As a result of the committee's recommendations the War Office established the Army Railway Council in 1897. This consisted of six representatives of the Staff Corps, three Board of Trade Inspectors of Railways (who were military officers), one regular officer, who acted as secretary, and a president nominated by the Secretary of State for War.

The creation of the Army Railway Council removed from the Staff Corps one of its original functions, and its primary one. Officers of the Staff Corps served on the Army Railway Council and were replaced as they retired; the Council was reconstituted in 1903, mainly because of the need for Admiralty representation on it. At the same time the Staff Corps representation was increased by two railway managers, the number of Board of Trade Inspectors was cut to one, and two naval officers were added. Soon afterwards it was renamed the War Railway Council, and lasted until about 1910, when, after several changes in Government policy, the Railway Executive Committee was eventually created. Railway managers were members of this in their own right, not as representatives of the Staff Corps, and from 1910 onwards the Staff Corps had nothing to do with the organisation or construction of railways in war.

This sorry tale reflects little credit on those charged with the defence of the realm. However, the Staff Corps played a most useful role. There is little doubt that the smoothness and efficiency with which mobilisation was carried out in 1914 and the Expeditionary Force was despatched to France were the direct outcome of the work undertaken by the officers of the Staff Corps on the Exercises during the first 20 years of its existence.

In January 1897 the Commandant of the Staff Corps received a letter from the Inspector General of Auxiliary Forces saying that the Commander-in-Chief of the Army, Lord Wolseley, had suggested that a reserve of reliable railwaymen was required to supplement, in war, the small railway cadres maintained by the Corps of Royal Engineers in peace. The Inspector General thought that it was most logical for these railway servants to be recruited by railway general managers who were Lieutenant Colonels in the Staff Corps, under the general supervision of the Commandant. It was not proposed to give military training to the Reservists because the Inspector General felt that discipline among railway employees was very strict and that any further training was unnecessary; training in drill and the use of arms could be deferred until after mobilisation.

At a special meeting of the Council of the Staff Corps on 9 February 1897 a sub-committee was formed to 'make further enquiries at the War Office as to the proposed scheme'. Despite two reminders from the War Office the sub-committee did not report until April 1898. The delay had occurred because of the difficulties experienced 'in face of the regrettable spirit of unrest that had been present for some months past and still existed among large bodies of railway servants'.

The sub-committee commented that the War Office's proposal had not mentioned the large proportion of railway employees who had previously served with the Colours and were still members of the Reserve Forces. The sub-committee estimated that the railways with which its members were connected already employed some 4,000 First Class Reservists and that a similar number were probably employed on other railways. The sub-committee argued that if these men were called up railway services would be seriously disrupted. Therefore the sub-committee suggested that a maximum of 25 men from each of four main classes (drivers and firemen; fitters; platelayers; traffic) should be provided by each of the 13 railway companies represented in the Staff Corps.

The War Office issued a scheme in October 1898 allowing applications for enlistment in a Reserve of Railway Tradesmen from men of the various railway companies through the agency of the Staff Corps. Men were to be enlisted for three years with the Colours and three years in the Reserve, but would be transferred to the Reserve immediately on enlistment. A Reservist would be discharged if he quitted railway service.

The Reserve had originally been planned to contain 300 men, sufficient to form two military railway companies. However, when the War Office authorised its formation on 17 October 1898 the number to be enlisted was limited to 50. Although the railway companies submitted many names even that small number proved difficult to raise, probably because many volunteers failed to reach the

Steam sappers during the Boer War, partly manned from the Reserve of Railway Tradesmen.

An armoured train during the Boer War. The Royal Engineers were heavily involved in repairing the railways in South Africa and in introducing armoured trains.

required standard of fitness. The Staff Corps did not keep any records of the Railway Reserve during the Reserve's first four years, nor was the Staff Corps informed about rejections or discharges; as a result, the proposed proportion of men to be provided by the 13 selected railway companies was not adhered to. By 1899 40 per cent of the Reserve came from the small North London Railway, while some of the major railway companies had not provided any men at all.

The Railway Reservists were called to the Colours on 7 October 1899, four days before the outbreak of the Boer War. Twelve men were distributed between 8 and 10 Railway Companies RE and 12 and 37 Field Companies RE; 12 were posted to 31 Fortress Company RE, which was converting to a Railway Company; and 20 went to 45 Fortress Company RE, which was forming at Chatham especially for the role of operating steam road transport in South Africa. One Reservist died at

Bloemfontein, 17 were invalided home, four took their discharge in South Africa in order to join the Government railways there, and the remainder returned home in 1902.

Some recruiting continued after the end of the Boer War. However, for reasons that are unknown today and appear to have been unknown to the Staff Corps at the time the War Office ceased recruiting in March 1908. The Reserve of Railway Tradesmen withered, and eventually died in 1913.

Chapter Four

Falling into Disuse

1886–1945

The Staff Corps was founded in the days of Empire, when the bulk of the British Army was serving overseas. According to the fashionable 'blue-water' theory, a powerful Navy made a successful foreign invasion virtually impossible, and as a result minimal land forces were required at home. It has already been seen how the sudden realisation that a hostile power could invade came as an unwelcome surprise and had much to do with the formation and early days of the Staff Corps. To use today's terminology, the Staff Corps was invented to do some planning for the defence of the homeland in a general war. Yet the thrust of successive Governments' policies was that a general war directly affecting the homeland would not take place.

During the nineteenth century the bulk of the Royal Engineers were abroad, supporting the British Army and the Empire by designing and constructing roads, railways, canals and so on. Not surprisingly contact between the Staff Corps, who served as Volunteers under a Lord Lieutenant, and the Corps of Royal Engineers, who came under the War Office, was non-existent. The Staff Corps' terms of reference meant that there was little need for dialogue. On the very few occasions they were meant to liaise, they appeared to treat each other with disdain.

After working on the Exercises, and contributing to the debate on railway operations in war, there was little the Staff Corps could do of its own accord. In turn the War Office asked nothing of it. The concept of the formation of the Staff Corps, its composition and its rules all combined to make any further contribution to the military process most unlikely.

It had always been compulsory for railway traffic officers to resign from the Staff

Corps when they ceased to work for the railways (unless especially recommended otherwise). However no such restriction was imposed on the engineers and contractors. It is therefore not surprising that the Staff Corps, as a self-regulating body of some of the most eminent engineers in the land without any duties to perform, became virtually a dining club for the great and the good of the Institution of Civil Engineers. Most of the 12 original engineers retained their commissions until they died, which was seldom before they were 80; one had to be persuaded to resign when he was 86. On only one occasion was a recommendation by the Commandant for a Staff Corps commission for an eminent engineer rejected; that was in 1900 when the Secretary of State wrote that 'it is felt that the age of 72 is beyond the limit at which a first appointment to the Corps should be made.'

The Staff Corps did not play any part in the Boer War in South Africa. However, that War had a profound effect on the British Army and eventually on the status of the Staff Corps as well.

Almost half a million men from all over the Empire took three years to defeat 35,000 largely untrained Boer farmers. The British soldier was as courageous and resourceful as he had ever been. It was therefore concluded something must be wrong with the Army, or with its Generals. The government established the Esher Committee to advise on the organisation of the Army. Lord Esher's report, presented in spring 1904, laid the groundwork for the British Army's second great reformer (after Cardwell). This was Richard Haldane (later Viscount Haldane), who became Secretary of State for War in the Liberal Government that took office in December 1905.

The most important elements of Haldane's reforms were the creation of a properly trained General Staff and the separation of the three functions that had previously been the responsibility of the Commander-in-Chief, a post that was now abolished. Policy became the responsibility of a new body, the Army Council, based in the War Office. Administration became the task of a newly formed organisation of Districts across the country, and the Field Force was left to train and prepare itself for war.

Haldane introduced an Army of two distinct but parallel and complementary parts. The Regular Force, supplemented by the Reserve, provided divisions for service overseas, while the Territorial Force, organised into divisions, was intended primarily to defend the United Kingdom. The Territorial Force also provided a means of training men for an expanded Regular Force, should that prove necessary. The Volunteers and the Militia ceased to exist.

These reforms were implemented by the Territorial and Reserve Forces Act 1907. The following year a Special Army Order stated that the Staff Corps was to be administered by the War Office under the title 'The Engineer and Railway Staff Corps'. The old Volunteers had accepted men up to the age of 49 and they enrolled for an indefinite period; the new Territorial, by contrast, was to be a man in the prime of life and, like the Regular, would be enlisted for four years. The special requirements of the Staff Corps were not taken into account when the Territorial Force Regulations were drafted (and it is extremely doubtful that the Corps was ever consulted). However, after representations to the War Office, a dispensation for the Staff Corps appeared in the amended Regulations of 1910. These stated that Staff Corps officers:

● would not be subject to any age limit, though their retention after 65 would have to be agreed by the War Office
● were exempt from all examinations for promotion
● were exempt from attending annual training *and*
● would not be entitled to receive any outfit allowance.

So the Staff Corps was now part of the British Army. Its role remained the defence of the homeland, though coincidentally at the same time it lost responsibility for organising the railways for war.

The Staff Corps took very little part in the First World War. One hour after war was declared, a warrant was issued empowering the President of the Board of Trade to take possession of the railways of Great Britain. Control was to be exercised through an Executive Committee of the railway general managers, all of whom, bar one, were Lieutenant Colonels of the Staff Corps. Thus the most obvious duty the Staff Corps might have performed during the Great War was discharged in another way.

The Staff Corps received only two requests during the War. The first was to appoint a small committee consisting of two engineers and one contractor to advise the War Office on the organisation of the labour required to carry out entrenchments of positions covering London. The other was a 'follow-on' to the Reserve of Railway Tradesmen (see Chapter Three), which had been disbanded in 1913. The War Office asked the Railway Executive Committee to raise about 20 officers and 1,000 railwaymen to form a Railway Construction Force within the existing RE Railway Troops on the Western Front. Aware that the Staff Corps had done the work before and knew what was required, the Railway Executive Committee delegated the task to the Commandant of the Staff Corps. The work was completed in early 1915.

In 1921 the Annual Capitation Grant for 1921/22 was not received. When the Acting Adjutant of the Staff Corps made enquiries of the War Office, he was told that payment had been withheld pending a decision about whether the Staff Corps should be retained in the new Territorial Army. This matter had still not been resolved on 1 January 1923, when many senior railway managers became redundant on the amalgamation of 123 separate railway companies into four groups (the London Midland & Scottish, London & North Eastern, Great Western and Southern Railways), each with a virtual monopoly in its region.

The Commandant met the Adjutant General to discuss revising the rules governing the Staff Corps. He learned little except that the Quartermaster General would in future be responsible for the Staff Corps. Not until 1924 did the War Office decide to retain the Staff Corps, when it authorised a total establishment of 60 officers. Ten of these were to be Colonels, five railway general managers and five members of the Council of the Institution of Civil Engineers. In addition, all officers were now required to be actively engaged in their profession.

Very little of any importance happened between the two World Wars. In these years, the Officers Commanding, as they were now known, were all general managers of one of the main railway groups and as such extremely busy men. It is not surprising that Council meetings were very poorly attended. Indeed one Officer Commanding, Colonel Sir Herbert Walker, attended two Council meetings between 1914 and 1937 – one on 6 January 1925, when he assumed command, and one on 5 October 1937, when he announced his retirement.

When, two days before the outbreak of the Second World War, the Territorial Army was embodied and subsequently absorbed into the Regular Army, the War Office stated that the embodiment was not intended to apply to the Staff Corps. The full extent to which the Staff Corps had been sidelined only became clear when the Army Auditor refused to pay the annual Capitation Grant in April 1940. However, little if anything was done about this.

Lord Stamp, President of the London Midland & Scottish Railway, had been appointed Officer Commanding in March 1939. However, he was killed (together with his wife and eldest son) when a bomb struck his house at Bromley during an air raid on the night of 16 April 1941. An extremely talented and able man, he had been a Colonel in the Staff Corps since 1927 and Officer Commanding for over two years. However throughout this period he did not attend a single meeting of the Council of Colonels.

Colonel Sir James Milne, General Manager of the Great Western Railway, replaced Lord Stamp in July 1941. He discovered that there were a number of vacancies in the Staff Corps as a result of deaths or resignations, but that the War Office was refusing to make new appointments on the grounds that Territorial Army appointments were in abeyance. Colonel Milne got himself an interview

Sir James Milne, Officer Commanding from 1941 to 1948, who restored purpose to the Staff Corps after the Second World War.

with the Quartermaster General in the War Office, presumably with some difficulty. He pointed out how unfortunate it would be if the Staff Corps had to be disbanded, but that it could not function satisfactorily as it was then constituted. After that meeting the War Office sanctioned the payment of the Capitation Grant, which had been withheld for two years, and Milne was given the go-ahead to reconstruct the Staff Corps.

Milne now held a series of Council discussions and also had meetings, some quite difficult, with the Engineer-in-Chief and Director of Transportation at the War Office. By April 1943 he had won the Council's agreement to a new set of Rules, which the War Office approved in June the same year. Formerly the purpose of the Staff Corps had been 'for directing the application of skilled labour and of railway transport to the purposes of National Defence, and for preparing in time of peace a system on which such duties could be conducted'. In future its function would be 'to provide a body of skilled engineers and transportation experts to advise the War Office on such engineering and transportation matters as may be put before it'.

The new Rules stated that members would perform no military duties, would receive neither pay nor outfit grants and would not be permitted to wear uniform unless specially authorised. (When the outfit allowance was withdrawn in 1910 uniform for Staff Corps officers became optional.) All officers would resign on reaching the age of 65, and Colonels from transportation organisations had to resign if they left their employment. An engineering Colonel had to resign if he ceased to be a Member of Council of the Institution of Civil Engineers. Milne also introduced the Supernumerary List. This allowed officers who had to retire on reaching the age of 65, but who still had up-to-date expertise to contribute, to retain their links with the Staff Corps in a non-active capacity.

Colonel Sir James Milne now set about reorganising and recruiting a stronger and more relevant Engineer and Railway Staff Corps.

Chapter Five

The Post-War Years

1945–1981

With the new Rules in force, the new organisation set up, and an officer from the War Office's Directorate of Transportation attending meetings of the Council of Colonels, the Staff Corps was better placed than it had been for 50 years to respond to requests for assistance from the Engineer-in-Chief and the Director of Transportation in the War Office.

The first request came from neither of these two officers but from the Control Commission in occupied Germany. After the end of hostilities in Europe the Allies set up the Control Commission, which had separate organisations in each of the four occupation zones into which defeated Germany was divided. The head of the Transport Division in the British Zone had been Director of Transportation at the War Office during the War and knew well the capability of the Staff Corps. He wrote to Colonel Sir James Milne, the Officer Commanding, explaining that he needed 200 officers who were experts in roads, railways, inland water transport and shipping. The Staff Corps recommended that, since many of the men able to fill these new posts were already in uniform in all three armed services, it should provide lists of those now serving who would be suitable for the work. The offer was accepted and the positions were filled.

As part of the reconstruction of the Army after the War, the Director of Transportation asked the Council of Colonels for advice on the organisation and composition of the Transportation Units of the Royal Engineers in the re-created Reserve Army. The Engineer-in-Chief asked the Staff Corps to find specialists in road, railway and port construction who would be willing to accept Territorial Army commissions so that they would be available to assist in training the new

Construction Squadrons Royal Engineers (TA) which were to be included in the new Order of Battle.

In May 1946 the Staff Corps was asked to advise the Royal Engineers on the construction of roads in future operations. Civil practice was too slow and labour-intensive for war, and it had also been found that the plant available was not robust enough to cope with warlike conditions and heavy-handed soldiers. The problem was referred to a committee of officers concerned with road construction, either as engineers or as contractors. They in turn organised a joint technical committee and working groups of officers of the Staff Corps and representatives of the War Office, the Ministry of Transport and the Road Research Laboratory. Within a year they produced a series of draft specifications, including methods of rapid road construction, and specifications for blacktop material for use on roads and airfields in war. All these were adopted by the Corps of Royal Engineers.

On 1 January 1948 the railways in Great Britain were nationalised. Colonel Sir James Milne, who had been General Manager of the Great Western Railway, had to retire. In accordance with the Rules he resigned command of the Staff Corps, handing over to Colonel Sir William Halcrow, a civil engineer and Past President of the Institution of Civil Engineers. After only 18 months in post, Sir William had to resign on account of age, and Colonel Sir Eustace Missenden, General Manager of the Southern Region, was appointed to succeed him. He too had to resign in less than two years; Colonel V A M Robertson, a railway engineer, was appointed Officer Commanding on 26 May 1951.

The years from 1951 to 1954 saw a modest increase in the amount of advice the Staff Corps was asked to provide and this improved liaison between the Staff Corps and the Royal Engineers. Committees or working parties were established to examine such topics as pile driving equipment for the RE, the strengthening of road bridges for military use, and the storage and distribution of cement in the field. At this time too members of the Staff Corps began to be asked to vet drafts of RE manuals on civil engineering topics; this arrangement continues to this day.

Colonel Robertson had to resign on reaching the age of 65, and was succeeded by Colonel Sir John Elliot on 1 January 1956.

After further assistance had been given to the Royal Engineers to solve various problems, in 1959 the Engineer-in-Chief decided to invite selected members of the Staff Corps to occasional conferences to discuss matters of mutual interest.

This led to the decision to provide to the Corps lists of officers on the engineering side of the Staff Corps able to answer questions on specific subjects posed directly by authorised officers in the War Office. This arrangement led to better and more immediate communications between the Royal Engineers and the Staff Corps; only questions of policy had to be directed through the Acting Adjutant to the Officer Commanding or the Council of Colonels.

When the British Railways Board replaced the British Transport Commission in 1963, the Rules had to be amended again. A new rule was introduced limiting the tenure of command to a maximum of five years. In that same year Colonel A B B Valentine, a railway traffic man, was appointed Officer Commanding and Major Douglas Coode, a civil engineer of Coode & Partners, took over as Acting Adjutant. Also in 1963, the McLeod Committee was established by the War Office to review the structure of logistics supporting the Army. The Committee recommended that a single Corps should be formed to cover every aspect of the Army's transport and movements (except construction). This led to the formation of the Royal Corps of Transport, and all the RE units involved in transport operations and movements were transferred and re-badged on 15 July 1965.

Colonel Alec Valentine held the post of Officer Commanding for less than two years; Colonel G A Wilson, a civil engineer, assumed command on 23 December 1964, the day after Valentine's 65th birthday. At last the Staff Corps had a younger commander; Colonel George Wilson was the first Officer Commanding affected by the 'five-year rule' introduced in 1963. He remained in command until December 1969, and then continued as an active Colonel for a further two years. Although very little was asked of the Staff Corps during the seven years covering the commands of Valentine and Wilson, links with the Royal Engineers were maintained and strengthened.

Colonel R Freeman, a civil engineer of Freeman Fox and Partners, was appointed to command in December 1969. Immediately after his appointment the Council of Colonels revised the Rules. Under the previous Rules Colonel Freeman would have been compelled to resign his commission when his term as Past President of the Council of the Institution of Civil Engineers expired; he had served as President from 1966 to 1967 at the early age of 55. Many of the other Rules were re-cast and their general arrangement was much improved.

Colonel J R Hammond took over command in December 1974 from Sir Ralph Freeman, but was allowed to serve for just over three years; he had to transfer to the Supernumerary List when he retired from service in the railways. His successor was Colonel Sir Kirby Laing, the first contractor to command the Staff Corps, and he remained Officer Commanding until July 1981.

The years 1970 to 1981 brought major changes to the Staff Corps and its operations as it gradually moved towards the organisation recognisable today. Contact between Staff Corps members and their colleagues in the Royal Engineers and later the Royal Corps of Transport took a more practical form after a meeting held in the Ministry of Defence in October 1971 (the War Office had ceased to exist in 1964) to discuss how members could best help the Regulars. In April 1972 the Engineer-in-Chief suggested to the Officer Commanding that expanding the expertise available in the Staff Corps to four new areas would benefit the work of his Department. The Officer Commanding set up a committee, with himself in the chair. The committee recommended to the Council that the Staff Corps should aim to have six members, irrespective of rank, experienced in each of ten general disciplines, and that all new entrants should be selected accordingly. The ten specialities were:
- roads and bridges
- docks and harbours
- railway civil engineering
- railway electrical and mechanical engineering
- water and sewage
- petrol and oil engineering
- mechanical and electrical engineering (other than railways)
- airfield design and construction
- geology and soil investigation
- management.
Engineer services was added later as an eleventh speciality.

The provision of advice to the newly formed Royal Corps of Transport was regularised and further specialities were added to the list in due course. In January 1974 the Council prepared a list of members with addresses, fields of expertise and experience overseas, and circulated it to selected senior officers of the Royal Engineers and the Royal Corps of Transport to enable them to contact any relevant member direct. The list brought more requests for advice, and it has been revised annually since then. However, it also became clear that many Sapper

Marchwood Military Port on the western shore of Southampton Water.

officers were unaware of the existence of the Staff Corps and of its collective expertise. It was therefore arranged that each year a senior member of the Staff Corps would give a talk on its functions to Regular Officers completing their Long Civil Engineering Course. These students have to present an 'end of course' paper, and the Staff Corps was also requested to provide expert critics; this arrangement proved so successful that it too continues to this day.

While awareness of the Staff Corps was growing in the two Regular Corps, within the Staff Corps itself regular contact was confined to the 30 Colonels and Lieutenant Colonels who made up the Council of Colonels. This meant that almost half the members did not know what was going on. In January 1976 Colonel Hammond

Airfield construction and repair in 1944, a far cry from today's more sophisticated methods.

initiated a twice-yearly newsletter with information about appointments, promotions, resignations, assignments undertaken, and other matters of interest. Members warmly welcomed this new means of keeping in touch.

During these years the breadth of the advice given and the places it involved was quite remarkable. Advice was provided on:
- breakwaters, moles, quay walls, piling for jetties
- crane foundations
- bridges, abutments, roads and route denial
- runway extensions
- water supply and treatment and sewerage
- power generation and air conditioning
- reinforced concrete chimneys and pre-cast concrete
- hovercraft
- the rebuilding of Marchwood Military Port.

All this in the following places: Christmas Island, Cyprus (including Akrotiri Mole), Gibraltar, Kenya, Nepal, Saudi Arabia, St Helena, Sudan and the United Kingdom.

The Staff Corps' longest-running assistance to the Royal Engineers has been its input into the development of the Sappers' capability for Airfield Damage Repair (ADR). This was not the kind of advice that caught much attention, in contrast with some future operational situations. But this continuing steady guidance for over ten years allowed the Royal Engineer Field Squadrons supporting the Royal Air Force to develop their drills and procedures to a state of internationally recognised effectiveness.

Although the RE did not lose its capability for airfield construction after the Second World War, the emphasis was on the basic 'expeditionary' fields needed in overseas campaigns. In 1964/65 the Royal Engineers assumed the responsibilities of the former Royal Air Force Airfield Construction Branch which had disappeared in a defence rationalisation measure. The 1967 Arab/Israeli War illustrated the problem very dramatically; the Israeli Air Force struck Egypt's permanent air bases at the outset and grounded the Egyptian Air Force almost completely. NATO considered the threat to large permanent bases so serious that in 1973 member nations were required to prove that they had capability to keep the main airfields open in the event of attack before they were granted NATO infrastructure funding for the bases.

High-performance air defence or strike aircraft, other than the Harrier, have high take-off and landing speeds and therefore need long runways with smooth, clean and accurately levelled surfaces. The RE conducted trials and experiments over a number of years in the search for the optimum solution. The Staff Corps contributed with advice and demonstrations on the repair of 'scabs' on the operating surface caused by rockets and airfield denial weapons. The concept of dynamic compaction for the rapid in-filling of bomb craters, the plant and

A Lightning fighter takes off with re-heat, illustrating the fierce effects military airfields have to stand.

Dynamic compaction trials for Airfield Damage Repair with shattered runway pavement in the foreground.

equipment required to do this, and the 'cap' to seal and restore the kind of surface required at the right strength: in all these matters the assistance of the Staff Corps was much appreciated. The problem of restoring damaged cabling and pipework on the airfields was also tackled.

While the Staff Corps worked on the shorter-term and practical aspects of the ADR problem, the Military Engineering Committee (a subsidiary committee of the Defence Scientific Advisory Council) studied the longer-term solution. Several members of the Staff Corps served on the Military Engineering Committee at various times. However, the Ministry of Defence disbanded that Committee, along with others, in a savings exercise during the 1990s. As a result the Staff Corps is now the only body able to give such important technical advice.

It took a long time to develop all the specialised techniques and equipment, but by 1980/81 the specialist Field Squadrons with an ADR capability were generally considered to be most effective for the kind of operations envisaged in western Europe. Some techniques designed for a future general war were useful in the Falklands operation, but none of the special plant or equipment was used in the Falklands because there was neither time nor shipping space to get it there. In the Gulf in 1991, when the intelligence was good and the deployment more orderly, the first field engineer units to deploy and the first to undertake engineer work were the ADR units responsible for RE support to the Royal Air Force.

Chapter Six

Operation Corporate

On 2 April 1982 the military junta ruling Argentina invaded and occupied the Falkland Islands, so bringing to an end years of diplomatic discussions and negotiations with Britain. The British operation to recapture the Islands was a most unexpected one, for after years of successive cuts in manpower, equipment and expenditure, as well as Government insistence that NATO was the top priority, the Armed Services were beginning to believe that they would never be asked to mount such an operation. The recapture was achieved at considerable cost to the Armed Services and only by adapting the tactics, techniques and equipment developed for north-west Europe to the most unusual circumstances of the South Atlantic.

The Ministry of Defence started to plan what would be required to hold and defend the Islands after recapture long before the first landings at San Carlos on 21 May 1982. It was clear that the Corps of Royal Engineers would face particularly difficult problems, because everyone would call on them to provide sophisticated or unusual facilities involving unfamiliar engineering in an underdeveloped archipelago 8,000 miles from any base. The Falklands represented the heaviest involvement of the Staff Corps in any operation since its formation, and it contributed to every stage from planning and policy to the execution of the engineering solutions. For the first time the Staff Corps gave Headquarters Engineer-in-Chief much helpful intelligence and advice about engineering matters very early in the planning process, so establishing a pattern for future operations.

Before the Argentine invasion, the Islands had a garrison of Royal Marines 30 to 40 strong in Moody Brook camp west of Port Stanley, the capital; there was also a

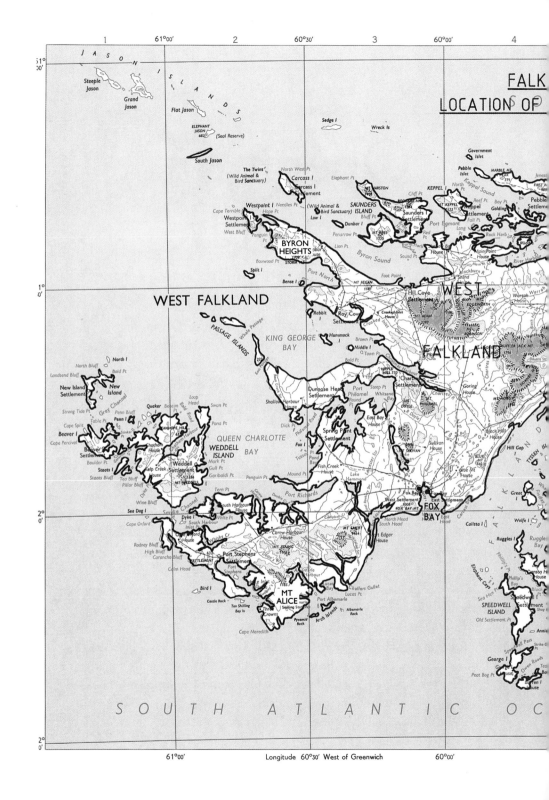

1   61°00'   2   60°30'   3   60°00'   4

51°00'

JASON ISLANDS

Steeple Jason

Grand Jason

Flat Jason

ELEPHANT JASON 682' (Seal Reserve)

South Jason

Sedge I

Wreck Is

Government Islet

Pebble Islet

MARBLE MT

The Twins (Wild Animal & Bird Sanctuary)

North West Pt

Carcass I

Carcass I Settlement

Elephant Pt

MT MARSTON

Cliff Pt

KEPPEL I

Keppel Sound

FIRST MT

Pebble

Reef Pt

Bay Pt

Pebble Settlement

Westpoint I

Needles Pt

(Wild Animal & Bird Sanctuary)

SAUNDERS ISLAND

Saunders Settlement

MT KEPPEL

Keppel Settlement

Golding

Cape Terrible

Hope Pt

Low I

Dunbar I

Bluff Pt

Port Egmont

Fall Pt

Rock Harb

Westpoint Settlement

West Bluff

Penarrow Pt

MT REES 1220

House

Rock Point

Mich

Penguin Pt

Lion Pt

BYRON HEIGHTS 1705'

House

Byron Sound

Sound Pt

House

Join Point House

River Harbour

Boxwood Pt

STORM

Port North

Mare

Blackburn R

Split I

Bense I

MT FEGAN 1181

Foot Point

Sound

Warra

WEST FALKLAND

Hill Cove Settlement

WEST

Worral House

EDGEWORTH

Rabbit

Roy Cove Settlement

Crookie Inlet

House

MT ADAM

FALKLAND

ROBINSON

PASSAGE ISLANDS

Whale Passage

Hunnmock

Crooked Inlet

SHUFFLER JACK MT 796

PENN I

North I

North Bluff

Bold Pt

KING GEORGE BAY

Middle I

Town Pt

Brown Pt

Bold Pt

Double Str

Chartres

Landsend Bluff

222

NIPPLE HILL 770

Charte Settlement

Chartres

Goring House

New Island Settlement

New Island

Strong Tide Pt

Grey Channel

Loop Head

Swan Pt

Shallow Harbour

Dunnose Head Settlement

Port Philomel

Whitsand

Steep Pt

MT DOYLE

PHILOMEL

MEMORIAL

Table Pt

Penn Bluff

Quaker

Beacon

Bold Hill

Pana Pt

Philomel Road

East Bay House

Black Hill House

Cape Split

STANHOPE HILL

Dick Pt

QUEEN CHARLOTTE BAY

Fox I

Spring Point Settlement

Sullivan House

Hill Gap

Beaver I

Cape Percival

Chatham House

WEDDELL ISLAND

Mark Pt

Pond

Port Bay

MT SULLIVAN

Cletler Mt

Beaver Settlement

Kelp Creek House

Weddell Settlement

MT WEDDELL 1266

Gull Pt

Garibaldi Pt

Penguin Pt

Tussac

Fish Creek House

Lake Hammond

TISSEN

Boulder Pt

Staats Pt

Staats Bluff

Mound Pt

Great

Teo Bluff

Pillar Bluff

Tern Pt

Port Richards

Fox Bay

West Settlement

FOX BAY

East Settlement

FOX BAY

Wine Bluff

South Harbour Settlement

White Pt

Camilla

North Head

South Head

East Head

Calista I

Wolfe I

Ruggles I

Ruggles Bay

Sea Dog I

Smilie Channel

Dyke

South Harbour

Inlet Pt

Carew Harbour House

MT SANEY 1404

Mt Edgar House

Cape Orford

House

Cape Orford

Whisky Cr

MT YOUNG 710'

Elephant Cove

Rodney Bluff

High Bluff

Caracho Bluff

Port Stephens Settlement

Port Stephens

Cantarle Harbour

Phillip's Bay

Sea Hen Pt

Rextra Hill House

Calm Head

Eagle Inlet

1185

Lucas

Harbour

Chaffers Gullet

Lucas Pt

SPEEDWELL ISLAND

Speedwell Settlement

Bird I

MT ALICE

Sealing Station

Port Albemarle

Old Settlement

Annie

Castle Rock

Ten Shilling Bay Is

Albemarle Rock

The Crowns

Pyramid Rock

Arch Islands

George I

Speedwell Pass

Cape Meredith

Striko Cl

Owen Roads

Peat Bog Pt

Tussac

House

SOUTH ATLANTIC OC

2°00'

1°0'

2°0'

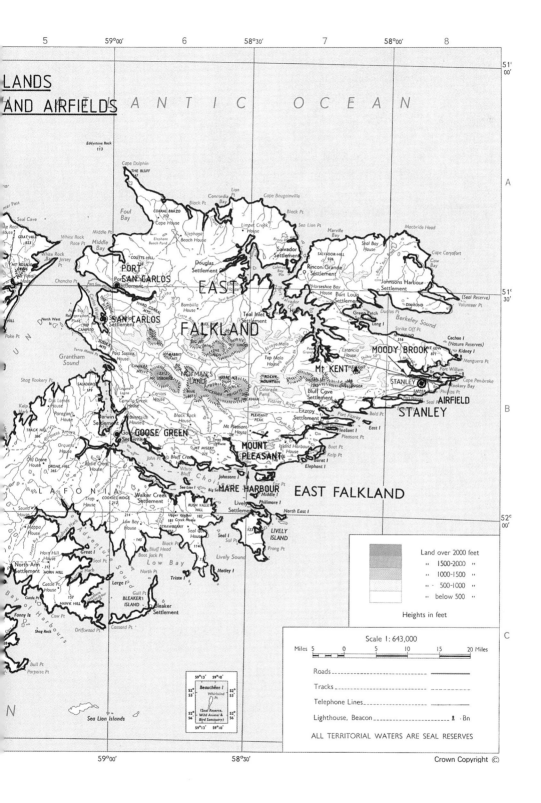

small civil airfield with rudimentary facilities to the east (see map on pages 48–49). After the recapture, the Chiefs of Staff required accommodation for hundreds of troops at various locations around the Islands, and a sophisticated modern military air base with all the things that go with it.

Stanley Airfield, constructed in about 1975 5 miles east of the town, had one runway 4,100 feet long and 150 feet wide; a single narrow taxiway connected the apron (275 feet by 130 feet) to the runway; the supporting facilities were fairly basic. It was obvious that the airfield would be a prime target for the Royal Navy and the Royal Air Force. Immediately after the invasion, the Staff Corps provided original drawings and construction details of the airfield. These proved of great value to the engineer planners in London, providing answers to vital questions, and later to the Royal Engineers on the ground after its recapture.

The only way to land modern high-performance aircraft very quickly on a runway that was not strong enough for them and would almost certainly have been damaged by our own action was to overlay the surface with an American 'expeditionary' aluminium mat. The Chiefs of Staff agreed to the immediate purchase of 150,000 square yards of AM 2 matting from the USA on 22 May, the day after the first landing.

It was essential to relieve as much of the Royal Navy Task Force as possible from the task of maintaining the defence of the Islands. This meant mounting surveillance and air defence from the land and also receiving reinforcements by air. The requirements laid down by the Chiefs of Staff were:

Phase One – immediately on recapture
● to repair and strengthen the existing runway, with an assumed LCN of 20 in parts, to allow its use by C130 Hercules aircraft in the maritime role by Day 5. (A Load Classification Number, LCN, is worked out for every aircraft, based on its weight, tyre pressures etc. Runways are designed to take a specific LCN. The lower the number, the lighter the load produced by the wheels on landing and take-off. Aircraft with a higher LCN than the runway should not land on it.)
● to install Rotary Hydraulic Arrester Gear by Day 9 to allow the operation of six Phantoms in the air defence role, and by Day 11 to allow operations by three Hercules, twelve Phantoms and six Buccaneers.

Stanley Airfield shortly after the Argentine surrender, littered with
wrecked aircraft and debris, before all the POWs departed.

Phase Two – from Day 11 to Day 22

● to lengthen the runway to 6,100 feet with a turning circle at one end to a
strength of LCN 45 to allow the operation of Nimrod aircraft at low weight to
replace the C130 Hercules in the maritime role.

● to build 22 cubic metres of additional fuel storage, an apron five times larger
than the existing one, three dispersals for Phantoms and Harriers, and provide
hangars, lighting and road access.

Phase Three – by Day 52

● to lengthen the runway again to 7,100 feet with turning circles at both ends.
There was also discussion about constructing a cross runway at a later stage.

All this was to be achieved while flying operations took priority on the
construction site, with the AM 2 mat in place, and on a site of considerable
engineering difficulty with widely scattered mines nearby.

The first Royal Engineers' reconnaissance of the captured airfield took place on
17 June, even though it was being used by the Land Force Commander as a
prisoner-of-war compound (see photograph above). It was decided to do the first

The first C130 Hercules coming in to land on the northern half of the runway at Stanley Airfield on 24 June. Wrecked Argentine aircraft still litter the southern edge.

The first C130 Hercules touches down after the aluminium matting had been laid.

of the immediate repairs in two halves. After the POWs departed, by clearing much debris and working 24 hours a day the northern half of the runway was repaired sufficiently to allow the first C130 Hercules to land on 24 June.

The repairs to the more badly damaged southern half took eight days to complete, interrupted by very bad weather and delays while men and equipment were moved out of the way to allow C130s to operate. Work then continued to strengthen and lengthen the runway and to make the other urgent improvements required.

On 28 July Ministers called for a plan for an airfield that could accommodate 'wide-bodied jet aircraft', with a runway up to 11,000 feet long. The first of a number of joint RE/RAF teams flew to the Islands to examine the options. As HQ Engineer-in-Chief moved forward with planning the construction, it became obvious that developing the airfield would take years rather than the weeks called for. This came as a deep shock to all in Whitehall (except the Property Services Agency, PSA).

At some stage in the late summer two entirely political factors became apparent. Both complicated planning a great deal and seemed to make little engineering or financial sense. First, the Royal Engineers alone were to build the new strategic airfield; in order to do so, they would be allowed to form new Field Squadrons and recruit hundreds of men to fill them. Second, the airfield was to be at Stanley. However, HQ Engineer-in-Chief was convinced that it would be quicker, cheaper and easier to build the strategic airfield away from Stanley and leave the existing airfield repaired and strengthened but not lengthened. HQ E-in-C had already done outline studies of the geology and other matters to identify a better site.

In October or November it was at last agreed in Whitehall to involve the PSA in siting the airfield and its representatives joined the reconnaissance teams still examining the problem. The Engineer-in-Chief was convinced that the Stanley site was not the best location for a strategic airfield. But Ministers wanted to use Stanley, and the Engineer-in-Chief still had instructions to build it with uniformed Sappers. In November he found that no one in Whitehall would accept his professional advice. Before he took his case to either the Chiefs of Staff or the Secretary of State for the last time, he needed a second professional opinion to ensure that he and his staff were talking sense and had not committed a major error of judgement. Even had he wanted to, he could not have approached an outside consultant, because he was at total odds with Government policy. He

Mount Pleasant Airfield constructed at March Ridge to take heavy and long-range aircraft. The runway is approximately three times the length of Stanley Airfield.

therefore turned in confidence to the Staff Corps and asked it to judge the engineer plans that his Headquarters had prepared for the construction of the strategic airfield.

The Staff Corps immediately appointed a team of four members, all experts in airfield design or construction, who attended a briefing in HQ Engineer-in-Chief and took away the plans so far made for detailed and critical scrutiny. (The team was led by Colonel Ken Scott; other members were Colonel P Cox, Lieutenant-Colonel L Rodger and Major J Taberner.) On 9 December Colonel Scott returned a detailed and most helpful critique to the Engineer-in-Chief. It is worth quoting two extracts from the report:

> In order to arrange the necessary supplies of equipment and materials, taking into account the communications difficulties, it will be necessary to complete the majority of the detailed design and working drawings before the start of construction. It is estimated that some 70 to 75 technical design staff will be required to produce the 800 to 1000 drawings and associated documents in a period of six or seven months.

And

> On the basis of the overall assessment of the proposed scope of the works, it is considered that the total programme is reasonable using army personnel. However, the anticipated construction period could be described as not less than four years, rather than a bald five years.

Colonel Scott also delivered a confidential covering letter in which he made two additional, and highly important, points not concerned with the Royal Engineers' plans:

> The wisdom of trying to absorb the design and construction of this major project within the activities of the Corps is, to say the least, extremely doubtful. [He listed the difficulties.] It does seem to be totally wrong that, at a time when there is a surplus of experienced UK staff and labour with adequate plant resources, these should not be used for such a scheme. Also we are confident that the use of the private sector would substantially reduce the real cost of the project and reduce the construction period to less than three years.

Armed with advice from the Staff Corps, the Engineer-in-Chief convinced the Secretary of State that his professional advice was correct. Government policy was reversed within hours. Colonel Scott, who had been on stand-by to brief the Secretary of State, was stood down. The PSA immediately began to finalise the design of, and put out to tender, a project to build a strategic airfield at March Ridge, at a site first recommended by the Royal Engineers (see photograph opposite). March Ridge was near a suitable deep-water anchorage at Mare Harbour, where bulk fuel for the airfield could be delivered; it was reported to be better and deeper than Stanley harbour.

As soon as work began on repairing the damaged airfield at Stanley, demand for crushed stone increased. What passed for roads around Stanley and the airfield also desperately needed stone as the huge increase in traffic and the atrocious weather were quickly turning them into seas of mud.

A small quarry was opened within days of the recapture. It was a poor site, but it was the only accessible one at the time. A better quarry was opened in August,

Maryhill Quarry near Port Stanley, operated by the RE. In the
upper picture are Colonel John Kitching, CRE Falklands (on the
left) and Ian Campbell, Officer Commanding of the Staff Corps.

on the site used by the civil engineering contractor who had built the original
runway. Before it could be used, 3 metres of water had to be pumped out and it
had to be cleared of the unexploded ordnance the Argentines had dumped in it.
The rock was fine-grained quartzite, very hard and abrasive, which made drilling
and crushing major problems – the crusher jaws were unable to cope with the
rock. It was also years since the RE had quarried on such a large scale.

In September 1982 Major S C L Hobden of the Staff Corps responded to a
request for help and, accompanied by an officer from the Engineer Specialist Pool
RE TA, made a two-week visit to the Falklands to give on-the-spot advice on
quarrying and geotechnical matters. The call for crushed stone increased
alarmingly as the Royal Engineers undertook more and more construction. Major
Hobden visited for another fortnight in late November. Besides giving much

practical help on existing and future quarry operations and stone-crushing, he also took part in a reconnaissance to examine some very difficult sites on West Falkland, advising on road repair and devising methods of securing holding-down bolts for anchoring buildings. Further advice was given during extended visits in early 1983 and in 1984.

Conditions could hardly have been more difficult for the Royal Engineers. Ultimately, however, the quarrying operation proved successful, with significant help from the Staff Corps and also from the industry in the UK, which advised on quarrying equipment.

Immediately after the invasion temporary accommodation had to be provided urgently for all the British forces on the Islands before the sub-Antarctic winter set in. Detachments of troops were scattered all over East and West Falkland for defensive purposes, and it was clear that the number of men based around Port Stanley would increase rapidly, as the airfield was improved and the forward base was established.

Two 800-man and seven 200-man 'Portakabin'-type camps were shipped from the UK, but were not due to arrive until late August. In the meantime, camps were designed and constructed using those stores that had survived the hazardous journey from a depot in Britain to off-loading at Stanley. The Royal Engineers asked the Staff Corps for advice on the unfamiliar equipment they were installing and on working in the very unusual conditions encountered in the Falklands. Assistance was given on electrical problems in switch-gear, on diesel engines, on the electrical protection of power plants, and on matters concerning water supply. Advice and on-the-spot assistance were invaluable in designing anchorages to hold down structures to resist the very large overturning moments from the strong winds common in the Islands.

By early August it was clear that the number of servicemen to be accommodated would be well above the guidance figures the Ministry of Defence had supplied in May. A quick and attractive way of providing more and better accommodation was to hire or buy 'coastel' barges; eventually there were three of these in the Falklands. These barges were five-storey floating hostels, each for over 900 men, designed for inshore waters (see photographs on page 58). They came complete with power, heating, fresh water, sewage disposal, laundry facilities, kitchens and dining-rooms. They had to be towed to the South Atlantic. The first

'Coastel' floating hotel barge moored near Port Stanley.

Staff Corps visit to a 'coastel'.

arrival was moored in the Canache, just east of Stanley harbour, on 12 January 1983 and was formally opened by a visiting Minister of Defence on 20 January.

Although this was a simple solution for the Ministry of Defence, it was very different for the Sappers on the ground. Both the seabed beneath and the land area around the coastel had to be cleared of unexploded ordnance; old wrecks had to be removed from the seabed as well (see photograph opposite). Then about 1 mile of road had to be constructed across very peaty ground to reach the mooring site and the coastel. The construction of the berthing face, designed to withstand very large wind loadings on very poor ground, was accomplished after much improvisation. However, the construction of eight permanent mooring bollards, to take loads of 100 tonnes, and of berthing dolphins caused the RE real design headaches and had to be put in the hands of the Staff Corps. It mobilised the UK's most experienced maritime engineering firms to solve the design problems and produce plans from which the Royal Engineers could work. Once the initial work was completed, the tide-tables provided were found to be inaccurate, and the Staff Corps gave further help on wind and tide forces before the second coastel was positioned in the Canache.

The need to relieve the Navy of defensive tasks that could be carried out more effectively or more cheaply from the land has already been mentioned. The Royal Navy had one particularly hazardous and demanding role: to provide early warning frigates in the South Atlantic between Argentina and the Falkland Islands where vessels were under threat from air and sea and also from under the sea. High-powered land-based radar could replace those early warning frigates, and the decision was made to install such radar on the top of Mount Kent during the brief sub-Antarctic summer of 1983. This became known as Project Zeus. Initially a sophisticated two-storey building on the summit was specified, 1,504 feet high in a most inhospitable climate on a very rough area. Because access was so difficult and time so short, the Air Staff settled for what was possible. This was after the Royal Engineers had again consulted the Staff Corps on how to hold down

The site in the Canache where the 'coastel' was moored.

Work in progress on Project Zeus, to construct mountain-top radar stations.

structures on the top of very windy mountains and how to create sound, secure earth-anchors in rock that varied from extremely hard to shattered fragments. Further radar stations were constructed at Byron Heights, 1,385 feet, on the far north-west peninsula of West Falkland, and at Mount Alice, almost 1,200 feet, on the southernmost promontory of West Falkland.

Chapter Seven

An Interactive Corps

1981–1990

Colonel I M Campbell took over command of the Engineer and Railway Staff Corps on 21 July 1981. Deputy Chairman of the Board of British Rail and President of the Institution of Civil Engineers, Ian Campbell was a man of great energy and enthusiasm. He was convinced that the Staff Corps could offer much more to the two Regular Corps it now supported, the Corps of Royal Engineers and the Royal Corps of Transport (RCT). He quickly organised a pamphlet (a first for the Staff Corps) to tell those concerned in the Ministry of Defence and the two Regular Corps about the Staff Corps and what it could do. He also floated the idea of regular liaison with the RE and RCT to improve the flow of information and generate greater interaction.

Colonel Douglas Coode, who had served as Acting Adjutant since 1963, was now over 70 and wished to retire after long and successful service. Major J P Taberner, then with Costain Civil Engineering, was persuaded to take on the job, comforted by Douglas Coode's assurance that provided he had a good secretary the demands on his time would not be great. It proved very different. John Taberner began a gradual takeover in 1982, and was formally appointed Lieutenant Colonel and Acting Adjutant on 16 January 1983.

The Falklands campaign interrupted John Taberner's takeover and slowed progress on creating an interactive relationship between the Staff Corps and the Regular Corps. In the long run, however, the War greatly benefited the Staff Corps, as more people came to realise its value and capability. Campbell's suggestion of liaison groups was discussed at length at two meetings of the Council of Colonels. The two Regular Corps agreed and also accepted Terms of

Reference produced in April 1983. These stated that the liaison groups were:

1. To meet with Officers of the RE and RCT at suitable intervals for discussion on matters of current and potential joint interest and concern;
2. To consider how the combined expertise within the Staff Corps can best be applied to assist the RE and RCT with identified problems;
3. To discuss with the RE and RCT the development or extension of new techniques which might have application to the operations of the respective Corps;
4. To report on the above matters to the Council of Colonels;
5. To keep the Acting Adjutant informed on the location, timing, proposed agenda and results of any meeting.

It was decided that each liaison group would be chaired by a Colonel and would consist of four or five Staff Corps members expert in either engineering or transportation issues. Each group was also to include Majors, who until then had been relatively passive members of the Staff Corps.

Ian Campbell realised that there was one other piece of modernisation that he alone could propose with ease, being both Officer Commanding and Deputy Chairman of British Rail. This was to drop the word 'Railway' from the Staff Corps' title and substitute 'Transport'. This change would reflect the roles of the two Regular Corps the Staff Corps was now supporting. The name was officially changed on 1 October 1984 to the Engineer and Transport Staff Corps RE (V).

After the 1984 Annual Dinner the Quartermaster General, General Sir Richard Trant, wrote to the Office Commanding to thank the Staff Corps for inviting him. He went on:

> We are indeed truly lucky that we have the support and ready advice that is on offer from the Engineer and Transport Staff Corps, the members of which are men eminent in their respective professions. May I, therefore, take this opportunity, as the Army Board Member within whose purview lie the activities which are most relevant to the service your Corps gives, to express our profound thanks for all that you do for us, which is so freely given too. Long may this association flourish.

The Transport Liaison Group held its first meeting on 15 December 1983 under the chairmanship of Lieutenant Colonel A T Pugh. Alastair Pugh was Managing

Director of British Caledonian Airways and the senior Staff Corps member serving the 'transport interest'. The Royal Corps of Transport reacted to the Transport Liaison Group very positively. The RCT was facing major changes of equipment and organisation, including a four-fold increase in ammunition rates for new weapons now coming into service. It was also keen to benefit from the management experience available in industry and commerce in running the Army's new logistic organisation. A series of regular meetings, at least two a year, between the Liaison Group and senior RCT officers started immediately. At one meeting, in June 1985, the RCT suggested occasional one- or two-day seminars at which the Liaison Group could give senior RCT officers a detailed insight into transport planning policy. From that suggestion developed a series of seminars on such subjects as:

- contingency planning
- management control and the measurement of effective management in contracting-out
- financial and budgetary control
- fuel supply in the field
- freight distribution
- warehousing
- asset-tracking
- training transport and distribution managers
- performance indicators
- port operating
- petroleum distribution and shipping
- the use of rail.

These seminars were always attended by a large number of senior RCT officers, often including the Director General and occasionally the Quartermaster General himself, and still continue. After one early seminar, the QMG of the day, General Sir Charles Huxtable, wrote to the Director General of Transport and Movements:

> Thank you for inviting me to your Seminar. I thoroughly enjoyed the day. I must say I thought the whole exercise very well worth while and that a number of very useful points came out – especially during the discussions on contracting in or out. In fact I thought a lot of what was said was

relevant to all contracting operations and not just in the question of administrative transport. I must say the Engineer and Transport Staff Corps is a most extraordinary organisation and one which it seems to me we are very lucky to have. I am so glad you have found such a good way for the Army to benefit from them.

The Engineer Liaison Group, established under the chairmanship of Colonel F A Sharman, held its first meeting on 1 March 1984. Andrew Sharman met a totally different reaction to the one that greeted the Transport Group. Quite why this was so was not immediately obvious at the time. Not long after he took over command from Colonel Ian Campbell on 30 April 1986, Colonel Terrel Wyatt said at a Council meeting that 'it would appear that the RCT is currently making much more use of the Staff Corps than the RE.' There were several sound reasons for this, and it is now clear that three factors contributed to the differing success of the two liaison groups in the early days.

Combat engineering is the primary role of the Royal Engineers – and with that goes the improvisation inevitable on operations. Although trained for civil engineering tasks in their widest sense, the Royal Engineers have few opportunities in peacetime to practise such engineering. By contrast, the primary peacetime task of the Royal Corps of Transport is much more analogous with civil operations. Hence the RCT was much more likely to call on the Staff Corps in peace and the RE to ask for advice in war, when the unusual was 'thrown' at them. The second factor is that the RE had been consulting the Staff Corps for many years when the liaison groups were set up, and well established links were already in existence. The third factor was that in its first six years the Transport Liaison Group had fourteen meetings and one Chairman, while the Engineer Liaison Group had six meetings and four Chairmen. The four Chairmen were all very good men and highly competent engineers, but the Staff Corps operated strictly on seniority and some became Chairman only months before retirement. In the same six years the Transport Group held six seminars, while the only significant assistance requested from the Engineer Group was to provide a Panel of Visitors to make a technical assessment of the Military Works Force of the Royal Engineers (see below).

Apart from this Panel of Visitors the Engineer Liaison Group did a good deal of work to assist the RE in the following fields:

- plant selection and procurement across their fleet of equipment
- information technology
- performance indicators
- materials technology
- whole life cycle costing.

The RE continued to make individual approaches for advice in the normal way via the Acting Adjutant (not the Liaison Group). These varied widely, and included the following among many others:

- bridge demolition
- specification and procurement of temporary accommodation
- repair of earthquake-damaged property
- slipway design
- field connectors for electric cables
- military power requirements
- concrete cutting equipment for rescue operations
- testing steel bridges
- geology.

While the Staff Corps is generally called on to provide expertise for training or to solve unusual 'one-off' engineering problems, it is capable of conducting much deeper studies if required. Three diverse examples illustrate how this capacity has been used to assist the Regular Forces in recent years.

The Demountable Rack Off-Loading and Pick-Up System (DROPS for short) was the military application of a bulk transportation system used in civil industry.

New artillery equipment was brought into service during the 1980s. In the light of the experience of other nations in high-intensity operations in wars in the Middle East, the Army carried out a detailed study of likely future battle attrition-rates and ammunition expenditure-rates. It found that the increased calibre of ammunition, the new multi-rocket system, and the amount of mines and explosive required for a defensive battle in north-west Europe could not be transported by the organisation that existed. Following a further study of the available options, it was decided that DROPS was the only distribution system capable of meeting the greatly enlarged task without an unacceptable increase in both manpower and vehicles.

A DROPS vehicle of the Royal Logistics Corps.

After the system had been ordered, to be in service in 1989, the decision was taken to examine other supply and transport tasks to discover whether DROPS could be utilised for them. By far the largest of these was the movement of fuel forward from the civil source to the tanks and vehicles on the battlefield.

The RCT started to investigate the idea of a DROPS-based fuel distribution system for a north-west European battlefield (see photograph above) and asked the Transport Liaison Group for its views. After an initial discussion, the RCT arranged for the Liaison Group to visit Germany for a briefing, demonstration and seminar, posing six questions for discussion. The Chairman of the Liaison Group and the Council of the Corps believed that many Staff Corps members, or their firms, had relevant experience. The questions were circulated to all members and responses were co-ordinated and discussed before the visit to Germany.

The seminar in the British Army of the Rhine proved very constructive. After further discussions with the Staff Corps and consideration in the Army, it was decided that DROPS was neither the best nor the most cost-effective solution to the problem, and fuel supply to the Army in the field continued to follow more conventional forms.

This study was unusual in that it represents the first occasion on which the entire Corps has been involved in answering a problem since the Exercises of 1865 to 1885 (see Chapter Two).

In 1989 the Director of Engineer Services in the Ministry of Defence decided that a review of information technology in the Military Works Force of the RE was urgently required, together with an evaluation of current applications and advice on possible future enhancements. It was thought essential to appoint as examiners engineers with specific experience in this particular field, rather than computer consultants. This was in effect a professional audit and technical assessment leading to advice on future development.

A number of members of the Staff Corps had up-to-the-minute practical experience in the use of information technology for small-scale design, quantity surveying and draughting. Three very senior members of the Staff Corps from the construction industry, under the chairmanship of Colonel Oscar Addyman, formed the Military Works Force Panel of Visitors to take on the task, assisted by an expert from one of their firms.

The Panel was asked to recommend possible improvements to the operation, organisation and computer-security of the Military Works Force's system and to examine the training of those who operated the system. Recommendations were also requested for the effective integration of a design and QS system and its associated software. The Panel of Visitors made a major contribution to the future development of the Military Works Force in its role as the in-house civil engineering consultancy of the Royal Engineers.

Since the early 1970s, Staff Corps engineers in the disciplines of geotechnics, geology and hydrogeology have been among the most often used and the hardest worked. Most of the tasks they have been assigned involve long site visits, sometimes in thoroughly unpleasant conditions as in the Falklands and Bosnia. These members have given the Royal Engineers invaluable advice and saved them much time, money and effort. Virtually all the problems posed to this element of the Staff Corps can be classified as studies in depth (no pun intended!).

To quote one very recent and typical example: at very short notice because of serious illness elsewhere, in September 1999 Lieutenant Colonel Rodney Chartres carried out a reconnaissance concerning Pokhara Camp in Nepal and submitted a report to the Military Works Force. The Camp is the location of the British Gurkha Garrison and the site of new offices and stores for the Gurkha Welfare Scheme. The immediate concerns were the stability of the side of the Kali Khola Gorge below the new offices and stores; the effect of surface water run-off and drainage on the site of the new build; and the stability of the side of the Kali Khola Gorge below the remainder of the Garrison and immediately downstream.

In his report Colonel Chartres examined the area's geology and rock properties, geotechnical properties and river hydrology. He surveyed the three mechanisms of failure on the side of the Kali Khola Gorge and the seismicity and glacial lake outburst floods that occur, and made a detailed inspection of the site of the new build office and store. His recommendations were designed to minimise the risk of the 'failure' mechanisms that he had identified, and he set out a programme of simple, practical measures to be taken by the resident staff in the Garrison to minimise the risks.

Chapter Eight

Operation Granby

When the eight-year Iran-Iraq War ended in 1988, Saddam Hussein's well equipped army was the fourth largest in the world; his air force was one of the most modern and operated from a large number of thoroughly hardened airfields. Years of heavy military spending and the need to repay massive overseas loans had left the Iraqi economy in a very poor state. In 1990 the slump in world oil prices, aggravated by over-production by certain other OPEC countries, reduced the country's revenues still further.

Iraq had long-standing claims on Kuwait and particularly on the Rumaylah oilfields on the border between the two countries. Saddam Hussein accused Kuwait of stealing Iraq's oil and of violating its OPEC production quotas. A short period of military build-up, fruitless negotiation and general confusion ended early on 2 August 1990 when Iraqi troops unexpectedly invaded and occupied Kuwait. Four days later Iraqi troops massed along the Saudi Arabian frontier.

The UN Security Council passed Resolution 660 on 2 August condemning the invasion and demanding immediate withdrawal. On 6 August it passed Resolution 661 imposing immediate sanctions on Iraq, to be enforced by an international naval force. This was the beginning of the military coalition that eventually ejected the Iraqi forces from Kuwait after Saddam Hussein refused to withdraw them.

The British contribution to the coalition force was called Operation Granby. For the British Army it became the largest conventional war operation mounted since the end of the Second World War. It was very different from Operation Corporate in the Falklands, for it used the tactics, procedures and equipment that

An armoured bridge layer on a tank bridge.

had been practised so often in the British Army of the Rhine – even though desert conditions made operations much more difficult, especially for everyone concerned with logistics. For the Royal Engineers the contrast with Operation Corporate was enormous. In the Falklands they had been called upon to do some very unusual tasks for military engineers, with virtually no time to plan, prepare and train. For Operation Granby they had time to plan, prepare and train, and their main tasks were those they had long trained for in peace: namely breaching minefields, crossing obstacles, route construction and maintenance, field accommodation and hospitals, fuel pipelines and airfield support. Well over one third of the Corps of Royal Engineers were deployed in the Gulf at some time or other.

Not surprisingly the role of the Staff Corps was also quite different from the one it played in the Falklands campaign. During and after the battle there were no calls for advice or assistance. That said, the Staff Corps did give invaluable assistance, in particular through its contribution to information and intelligence. However all this happened during the preparatory phase and was incorporated into planning and training before battle was joined.

Very soon after the Iraqi invasion members of the Staff Corps from the oil and construction industries provided full and very valuable information on the construction of oil pipelines and how to cross them with heavy vehicles. They also advised on the burning-rates of various crude oils, on the vapour hazards to be expected, and on the consequences of major spillages in different conditions. Armed with this information the RE and the Royal Armament Research and Development Establishment at Christchurch were able to set up studies and trials to meet the challenge of dealing with oil fires and oil-filled anti-tank ditches and crossing pipelines. A modification was devised for both the No8 and the No9 tank bridges so that they could be used for crossing pipelines, and the Medium Girder Overbridge was adapted for the same purpose. A special vehicle-mounted device was also designed and produced for dousing oil fires in large trenches when a tank bridge crossing was being made; in the event this was not required.

The Staff Corps also contributed very important information to the Logistic Intelligence Brief produced for the British forces to assist both planning and actual operations. This included information on terrain and going, oil

Bridge layer crews prepare for battle.

An armoured bridge layer crosses a burning oil ditch during training.

wells, oil installations, electricity generation and transmission, water supply and construction resources in the area.

The campaign to liberate Kuwait lasted 42 days and the land war took only 100 hours to complete. In relation to the size of the operation, the coalition sustained very light casualties, especially considering the scale of operations, the strength of the Iraqi defence position, and the size of the enemy forces. Very good intelligence and good preparation were key factors in the coalition's success.

Chapter Nine

A Flourishing Staff Corps

1990–2001

At the start of the 1990s the nature of the relationship between the Staff Corps and the two Corps of the Regular Army changed markedly. No single event was responsible for this change, but rather a number of factors that came into effect over a relatively short period.

From the perspective of the Staff Corps, the most important factor was its two very effective, proactive Liaison Groups, which made a real contribution to the Royal Engineers and the Royal Corps of Transport. The capabilities of the Staff Corps were becoming more widely known in the Regular Army not only through these Liaison Groups but also because of involvement in the two largest operations of the previous ten years: the Falklands War and the Gulf War. At the same time, the Army was being subjected to ever more stringent financial cuts; had a new management structure; was having to reorganise to achieve savings; was contemplating private-sector involvement in activities that until then had been purely military; and was increasingly adopting the methods of modern civilian management.

So the Staff Corps became an appropriate and friendly organisation to approach for advice or with which to float ideas. It had a wealth of expertise across the areas relevant to the two Regular Corps, and, what was more, it was free!

Colonel Terrel Wyatt had commanded the Staff Corps since 1986 and Colonel John Taberner had been Acting Adjutant since 1982, so the Corps entered the 1990s and the new situation with a command team of great experience. They broke with tradition and appointed a Chairman for the Engineer Liaison Group who could serve for a long time and bring the same continuity and stability to that Group as its Logistic counterpart had enjoyed since its formation. Indeed, the boot was now on the other foot because of the numerous reorganisations in the Army and the turbulence of postings, particularly on the logistics side; the minutes of the Staff Corps contain a complaint from a Liaison Group Chairman that he had just been given his fifth name as 'point of contact' officer in two years. On 1 November 1991 Colonel D J Lee, Chairman of G Maunsell and Partners, took over command from Terrel Wyatt.

One of the many studies in the Army in 1990/91 was the Logistic Support Review. This recommended that there should be only two principal support functions: equipment support and service support. As a result the Royal Electrical and Mechanical Engineers became responsible for all equipment support on 1 April 1992. A new Corps to provide all service support was formed on 5 April 1993 by amalgamating the Royal Corps of Transport, the Royal Army Ordnance Corps, the Postal and Courier Branch of the Royal Engineers, the Royal Pioneer Corps, and the Army Catering Corps; the title of this new organisation was the Royal Logistic Corps, abbreviated to RLC.

The Transport Liaison Group of the Staff Corps changed its name to Logistic Liaison Group almost immediately. However, not until November 1996 was the name of the Staff Corps itself changed to Engineer and Logistic Staff Corps RE (V), since formal approval from the Ministry of Defence was required. Until the formation of the Royal Logistic Corps, the Staff Corps had only four or five officers at any time covering railways, shipping, air and land movements, and petroleum handling and distribution. The new RLC wanted to learn about equivalent civil practices and embrace new functions, and so the Staff Corps increased to eight the number of officers covering these new specialisations.

Colonel John Taberner, who was Acting Adjutant when the Liaison Groups were first organised in 1984, attended the meetings of both Groups. As they became increasingly effective and involved, the workload of the Acting Adjutant grew correspondingly. Add to this the increasing number of requests for advice or assistance, largely from the RE, and it was obvious that the task was beginning to be onerous for someone with a full-time job. John Taberner was due to retire from the active Staff Corps in 1996, and it was decided that the load should be lightened. Lieutenant Colonel Mike Stancombe, then an Assistant Director of the Institution of Civil Engineers, took over as Acting Adjutant on 1 January 1994. He

74

had risen to the rank of full Colonel in the RE before entering civil employment and was a professional chartered engineer. His already wide knowledge of the RE and the Army in general would make life slightly easier and would certainly reduce the 'learning curve' of a new Acting Adjutant. To reduce the Acting Adjutant's work still more, the financial side of his task was transferred to the new post of Honorary Treasurer. Colonel John Taberner assumed this role on 1 January 1994, an appointment he still holds.

The regular whole-day seminars organised by the Logistic Liaison Group reflected the widening scope of the liaison with the RLC; they were usually attended by a very high proportion of the Corps' senior officers. The seminar themes included:

- logistic and supply chain management
- hub distribution
- perishable warehousing and distribution
- visibility and asset tracking
- the commercial view of partnering.

Many of these seminars, and also some of the major topics covered in meetings of the Logistic Liaison Group, were linked to visits arranged by Staff Corps members for Regular Officers. These were to such places as major distribution centres for foodstuffs and freight and parcels, large commercial warehouses, ports, and petrol and oil storage and distribution facilities.

Large seminars have never been a feature of the engineer side of the Staff Corps. Most business was discussed in the meetings of the Engineer Liaison Group; occasionally visits were organised for a specially selected team for a particular purpose. Examples of the many subjects covered by this Liaison Group are:

- project management
- energy from solar power
- the efficient use of energy
- GRP advanced composites
- civil affairs
- water treatment and processing systems
- demolition of buildings
- defence works services
- disaster relief
- visit to Royal Armament Research and Development Establishment.

The pattern of contact between the Royal Engineers and the Staff Corps had developed over some 30 years. It usually concerned either the training of Royal Engineers or advice or assistance on a specific engineering matter that fell outside their normal training and experience and on which Staff Corps members were much better informed. On the training side a member of the Staff Corps continued to brief students on each Long Civil Engineering Course on its capability and working methods, and the Staff Corps also continued to provide critics for the course technical papers. Professional and technical advice was also provided for the engineering pamphlets written for the RE, and members also helped to find placements in civil companies for officers studying civil, mechanical and electrical engineering.

The following selection of topics demonstrates the breadth of advice given to the RE during the 1990s:

● advice and design check on site for a roll on/roll-off project in Cyprus
● pollution surveys
● advice on a large retaining wall
● software for project management
● engineer resources
● assistance in improving a counter-terrorist search facility.

Chapters Ten and Eleven mention many of the requests for advice concerning Bosnia and Kosovo.

Increased involvement with the relevant Regular Corps has made the job of Chairman of a Liaison Group an onerous one. However, it is the most important factor in the successful and continuous co-operation between the Staff Corps and the Regular Army. It is doubtful that Colonel Ian Campbell realised how much work would fall to these Chairmen when he started the Groups in 1984. The Regular Army and the Staff Corps owe the various officers a large debt for their contribution over the years. The Chairmen during the years covered in this chapter were:

for the Engineer Liaison Group
Colonel Ken Dale to 17 December 1990
Colonel Oliver Whitehead to 5 October 1999
Lieutenant Colonel Gil Howarth currently.
for the Logistic Liaison Group
Lieutenant Colonel Jeremy Gotch to 14 July 1993

Lieutenant Colonel Paul Bateson to 9 May 1996
Colonel John Swanson-Smith to 23 June 1999
Lieutenant Colonel Kevin Williams currently.

Returning to the appointment of Officers Commanding, David Lee retired on 28 August 1995 and Colonel W Hogbin took over the next day. However Walter Hogbin was in command for less than 18 months, as he had to retire on assuming an appointment in the Far East. Colonel J R Hennessy took over on 19 February 1997. John Hennessy was at that time Vice Chairman of Gibb Ltd (formerly Sir Alexander Gibb and Partners). He was succeeded by Colonel Oliver Whitehead, Chief Executive of Alfred McAlpine, in February 2001.

In 1999, on the advice of the HQ Engineer-in-Chief, the Officer Commanding began to be referred to as the Commanding Officer in day-to-day business. This was largely to make the appointment better understood by the Regular Army. However formal agreement has yet to be given for this change of title.

Akrotiri Mole, Cyprus, under construction to provide an emergency harbour for the Western Sovereign Base.

Major Matthew Tresidder RE (right) receives the 1999 Engineer and Logistics Staff Corps Prize from General Sir Roger Wheeler, GCB, CBE, Chief of the General Staff, with (centre) Colonel John Hennessy, Commanding Officer of the Staff Corps.

In 1996 the Staff Corps decided to present an annual prize to be awarded to an officer (or non-commissioned officer) identified by the RE or the RLC who had made an outstanding contribution to the Army in the fields of either engineering or logistics. Originally the prize, an engraved glass bowl, was to be awarded to an RE officer and an RLC officer in alternate years. However, from 2001 a prize will be awarded annually to an officer of each Regular Corps. In 1997 it was awarded to Major Tony Wakeman RE, in 1998 to Major Richard Greathead RLC, in 1999 to Major Matthew Tresidder RE, and in 2000 to Captain Gillian Jenkins RLC.

The Engineer and Logistic Staff Corps Prize is given at the Annual Dinner of the Staff Corps each autumn, which is one of the few occasions when the whole Corps can meet socially. These dinners have been held since foundation, with some interruptions caused by war or the death of the monarch. Only in recent years have they taken on a distinctly military flavour, being held in either the HQ Mess of the Royal Engineers at Chatham or the Royal Logistic Corps HQ Mess at Deepcut, near Camberley. The other social occasion is the popular Ladies Dinner Night, started in 1984, which is held every three years in the spring.

Chapter Ten

The Collapse of Former Yugoslavia

Unlike the nation states of Western Europe, the states of the Balkans were created following the sudden and violent collapse of the old multi-national empires of central and southern Europe. Because of the historic pattern of settlement there are minorities throughout the Balkan states. President Tito, who died in 1980, used 'strong-arm' communist methods and occasional shrewd compromises to keep Yugoslavia united. Without Tito nationalism became the key issue for all the political leaders in the various republics that made up Yugoslavia. Nationalism deflected attention from the very poor economic conditions, focusing instead on a distant and glorious past that could be adjusted to fit each Republic.

Conflict erupted in June 1991 when both the Slovenian and Croatian Parliaments voted for independence; Serbia reacted by attacking Croatia. Cyrus Vance, the American diplomat, was charged by the UN to negotiate a ceasefire to allow the UN to deploy a peace-keeping force into Croatia. The UN designated four 'Protected Areas' along Croatia's borders, where there were historic Serbian settlements. A ceasefire was negotiated on 2 January 1992 and the UN Protection Force (UNPROFOR) came into being on 21 February, initially with a ground force 15,000 strong from 26 countries. This was the first UN peace-keeping mission in continental Europe; by the end of 1992, when 22,000 troops were involved, it had become the largest ever deployed by the UN.

British engineers and logistic troops deployed to Croatia with UNPROFOR. Their role was largely close support to the infantry and providing accommodation and maintenance for the British contingent. There were no calls upon the Staff Corps in this part of UNPROFOR.

The states of the former Republic of Yugoslavia.

Bosnia-Hercegovina was governed by a coalition representing the three main religious parties, led by a Muslim-Croat alliance under a Muslim President, Alia Izetbegovic. When in October 1991 a large majority of the Bosnia-Hercegovina Assembly voted in favour of independence for Bosnia-Hercegovina, the Serb minority threatened civil war. After a referendum on independence in February 1992 Izetbegovic declared independence on 5 April, and the Bosnian Serbs, assisted by the Yugoslav Army, immediately mounted a campaign of terror throughout Bosnia and attacked the capital, Sarajevo. Serb atrocities against Muslim civilians outraged public opinion in the 'West'. The UN's demand for the Yugoslav Army to withdraw from Bosnia was ignored and so the UN imposed comprehensive sanctions against Serbia and Montenegro. The United Nations High Commissioner for Refugees (UNHCR) made several attempts to get food and medicine to the many besieged communities all over the country, but was completely frustrated. A second element of UNPROFOR was then created to escort humanitarian aid in Bosnia. Initially called UNPROFOR TWO it was to be 7,000 strong, with headquarters provided by NATO.

Serbia continued to attack the Muslims and destroyed much of Sarajevo by shell fire. Lord Owen (David Owen, the former British Secretary of State for Foreign Affairs) now joined Cyrus Vance to try to negotiate a settlement. The Croat-Muslim alliance broke down because President Tudjman of Croatia reneged on his ally in an attempt to divide Bosnia between Croatia and Serbia. The Croatian Army and the Bosnian Croats attacked the Muslims and showed that they were as willing as the Serbs to commit atrocities against civilians. During this campaign the Croats destroyed the eastern part of Mostar, the capital of Hercegovina. In March 1994, under heavy international pressure, the two Presidents of Bosnia and Croatia were persuaded to form a Federation, which amounted to little more than a ceasefire, and the 'Five Nation Group' (the USA, UK, France, Germany and Russia) took on the task of finding a solution. A ceasefire between all the warring parties was eventually agreed in December 1994.

Military engineers and logisticians serving in Bosnia had a great deal to do to provide the British contingent serving with the UN peace-keeping forces with accommodation, close support and everything required to sustain a force in a shattered environment. However, because they were deployed to enable the UNHCR's humanitarian aid convoys to reach those in desperate need there was a very large commitment to roads and bridges. Seven major rail bridges had been blown up and mined, cutting all rail communications in and out of the country. War damage to buildings and road bridges was widespread. Six motorway and major road bridges had been demolished, making it essential to construct a new road from the Croatian coast through the mountains until the main routes could be reinstated. Personnel accommodation and supply camps and depots had to be 'hardened' against attack, and RE well-drillers provided a source of potable water at virtually every British camp and also at some others.

The Staff Corps was asked to advise on the demolition of bridges and buildings and on reconstruction techniques, which were complicated by the degree of destruction (see photographs on page 82). This very important form of assistance to the RE force in Bosnia-Hercegovina continued until 1997. Many buildings in the Muslim sector of Mostar had to be demolished. One example will illustrate how the Staff Corps was able to help. A seven-storey reinforced-concrete block and its attached two-storey supermarket were in imminent danger of collapse.

A damaged bridge over the Vrbas River, Bosnia, and, below, Sappers constructing replacement bridging.

The local authority could not trace any construction drawings and the structure was too unstable to allow a technical reconnaissance. The RE proposed to implode the building into its own plan area with the minimum possible charges by attacking the structure at its critical points. The Staff Corps advised on the likely points where failure could be induced and on civil demolition techniques in city centres.

In late 1994 the Staff Corps was called upon to scrutinise the Royal Engineers' proposal for repairing and reactivating the high-voltage electrical distribution system in the Gornji Vakuf area in order to supply power to one of the main UN bases in central Bosnia. Although the RE rarely installs high-voltage systems in operational situations, a 20,000 volt HV solution was the most suitable to meet the power requirements of the two camps. These were situated in the former

Precision (car components) and TOM shoe factories; the pre-war power distribution network appeared not to have been greatly damaged or vandalised. All the comments made by the Staff Corps were incorporated into the RE plan.

In an attempt to increase the safety of the Bosnian Muslim civil population the UN declared six 'Safe Areas' which they said they would 'police'. These were at Sarajevo, Gorazde, Zepa, Srebrenica, Tuzla and Bihac.

Croatia refused to renew UNPROFOR's mandate in February 1995 and by the spring the ceasefire was breaking down. The Bosnian, Croat and Serb Armies prepared to go to war again. Mediation failed and the Bosnian Serbs and the Croats tried to finish by military action what they could not accomplish by other methods. The Bosnian Army tried to break out of the Serb encirclement of Sarajevo, the Croats occupied the four former 'Protected Areas' for Serbs on the Croatian border, previously guarded by UNPROFOR, and the Bosnian Serbs attacked the UN 'Safe Areas'. UNPROFOR TWO, charged with 'policing' the 'Safe Areas', was completely outgunned, and many informed observers believe that the UN Command issued confusing and impossible orders. The first attack was on Srebrenica where over 7,500 unarmed men were taken away and murdered. The Serbs next attacked and captured Zepa; the assault on the third 'Safe Area' at Gorazde was halted only by the threat of NATO air strikes against the Bosnian Serb Army and pressure from President Milosevic. On 28 August the Serbs launched a second mortar attack on the market in Sarajevo, the capital and a 'Safe Area'; NATO airstrikes against the Bosnian Serb forces led to the collapse of their campaign. The Presidents of Bosnia-Hercegovina, Croatia and Serbia signed the Dayton Agreement on 21 November 1995, to be upheld by a NATO led peace-keeping force known as the Implementation Force (IFOR). A year later this was succeeded by the NATO Stabilization Force (SFOR).

So great was the infrastructure damage that the Staff Corps continued to provide advice throughout this period. Quarrying was another continuing theme. The Royal Engineers had been conducting quarrying operations since their first deployment in Bosnia-Hercegovina. To begin with only small quantities of stone were required for road repairs and widening. As the NATO forces developed their role, demand increased. Camp construction, major route reconstruction, road maintenance, bridge repair and general repairs to war damage all required large quantities of crushed stone. Even before the fighting, local quarries had been neglected and badly run, and some completely new quarries were opened. In February 1995, through the offices of the Staff Corps, an expert from Taylor Woodrow International inspected 30 quarries in six days, despite the presence of mines and snow. For the next two years there was a continual flow of advice and visits by Staff Corps members to help the Royal Engineers supply the demand for stone.

In 1996 Walter Hogbin, the Officer Commanding, visited Bosnia-Hercegovina with the Engineer-in-Chief to assess what further help could be provided to the RE in the theatre.

In UN operations many nations contribute to the military force deployed, and military engineers from NATO countries and from the previous Warsaw Pact states served in Bosnia-Hercegovina. In early 1996 the British Chief Engineer of this multi-national force called upon the Staff Corps to evaluate a proposal for a Polish floating bridge to be used in re-establishing the rail system. Later that year he requested on-site advice about repairing a damaged geothermal well near Sarajevo; following the Staff Corps' proposals the well was successfully repaired.

Chapter Eleven

Kosovo

Kosovo has had a large ethnic Albanian majority for centuries. In recognition of this, President Tito granted autonomous status to Kosovo within the Yugoslav Republic. In 1989 the Serbian leader, Slobodan Milosevic, rescinded Kosovo's autonomous status, dissolved the regional government and began the systematic repression of the Albanian population. After the Dayton Agreement of December 1995 Kosovo Albanians looked with envy at events in Bosnia and Croatia. These two former regions had achieved international recognition, if not total independence; they had managed to halt Serb aggression; and now they were receiving international aid. In Kosovo, however, the Albanian majority was suffering under a Serbian police state with no sign of relief.

The rebellion in Kosovo started on 22 April 1996 when small groups of the Kosovo Liberation Army (KLA) launched four attacks on Serbs. Following the usual pattern it increased in intensity, but events in Montenegro hastened the inevitable full-scale revolt. Montenegro, a very small republic and Serbia's so-called partner in the new Federal Republic of Yugoslavia, had little interest in Serbia's wars; UN sanctions and international isolation as a result of Serbian aggression against Bosnia and Croatia were hitting Montenegro hard. As a result in October 1997 Montenegrins elected Milo Djukanovic, an outspoken critic of Milosevic, as their President. The Serbian leader now decided to stamp his authority on what was left of the Republic of Yugoslavia by defeating the KLA and by carrying out ethnic cleansing of the Albanians in Kosovo.

After much frustrating diplomatic activity and many broken agreements, the KLA eventually dropped its demand for outright independence and accepted that

Kosovo and the Federal Republic of Yugoslavia.

Kosovo would become an autonomous region, guaranteed by a NATO peace-keeping force. Following a UN Security Council Resolution, Milosevic had previously agreed a ceasefire with monitors from the Organisation for Security and Co-operation in Europe (OCSE). Now he stated that he would never allow any NATO presence within Kosovo. Milosevic was daring NATO to do something.

OSCE had been asked to monitor the ceasefire in Kosovo and with Milosevic's agreement had sent in an unarmed monitoring organisation. During the Rambouillet peace talks it was believed that these unarmed monitors could be at risk; they could be taken hostage by the Serbs or be used as human shields in a NATO attack; or it could be impossible to bring them out if the situation worsened. In December 1998 a multi-national Extraction Force was sent to Macedonia to be ready to rescue or support the monitors. The British part of this force was called Operation Upminster. It included a large number of engineers because both infrastructure and facilities were poor in Macedonia. When it was decided that ground forces might have to enter Kosovo to control or supervise a ceasefire a much larger NATO force was despatched to Macedonia, starting in February 1999. This was known as KFOR, the Kosovo Force. The British element went under the name of Operation Agricola. The OSCE monitors were withdrawn. The bombing campaign against Yugoslavia began on 24 March 1999 and KFOR troops entered Kosovo on 12 June.

The demands on engineers were heavy. The infrastructure requirement for Operation Upminster in Macedonia was followed by the much larger demand for the Operation Agricola force. And from Easter 1999 onwards into the summer came the totally unexpected task of building camps for the 30,000 refugees fleeing Kosovo into Macedonia and Albania.

After it became clear that British troops would have to deploy into Kosovo, the Staff Corps received two requests. Military Survey asked whether any members had access to large-scale maps that they could use to produce mapping of the area of operations; the Staff Corps duly responded. The second request was for any available information on hydrogeology and geology to help the Royal Engineers to find water for the troops and aggregate and roadstone from quarries. Gibb, the firm of the Commanding Officer, had staff in Albania, Bosnia and Macedonia and therefore knew a good deal about the region. It set up a 'desk-top study' from geological mapping and in consultation with others advised on what stone would be found, the best stone to use for construction, and, in general terms, where to find it. It also gave helpful warnings about using certain material and a good brief on water abstraction techniques.

The RE cleared the route ahead of the leading battle group into Kosovo. Having arrived it faced the expected tasks of providing accommodation for the British force and dealing with the major problem of mines, booby-traps and unexploded munitions and demolition charges. When KFOR reached Kosovo virtually no power was being generated, and the territory was totally reliant on imported electricity from Serbia and Albania. Although the transmission and distribution systems had been damaged during the fighting, years of neglect and lack of maintenance proved much more important. Albanians had been purged from all public-sector management jobs in 1990 and now most of the Serbs had fled. The two main power stations in Kosovo had been closed down for months and there was no capacity anywhere to fire a power station that required a 60 megawatt surge from elsewhere to start up. The United Nations Mission in Kosovo (UNMIK), which was to form the interim civil administration and take responsibility for public utilities, was in no position to take control in the early weeks. Restoring power was a very important part of the peace-keeping process, particularly in Pristina, the capital, where opportunities for murder, looting and intimidation were rife in a blacked-out city.

While the Chief Engineer's staff searched for experienced locals, the Staff Corps was asked for assistance. Lieutenant Colonel Roger Urwin (Managing Director, Transmission, of The National Grid Group plc) was contacted on Saturday 26 June; having concluded that a review at his level was appropriate he was in Kosovo in uniform on Monday 28 June for a 48-hour appraisal. He had warned his fellow Staff Corps member, Major John Baxter, Chief Engineer of Powergen, before leaving, and small teams were assembled in UK ready to fly out if required. The key to the restoring power to Kosovo was to bring one of the two big power stations back into operation while the major breaks in the transmission lines were repaired. A joint National Grid/Powergen team that flew out shortly after Lieutenant Colonel Urwin gave enormous help to the Sappers and civilians on the ground and played a crucial part in re-establishing power in Kosovo. Assistance to the power industry continued after the initial effort but under the auspices of the Department of Trade and Industry.

There was concern that a similar situation might be found in the local water industry. As a precaution Major Bill Alexander of the Staff Corps, Chief Executive

Exterior and generator floor of Kosovo A coal-fired power station.

of Thames Water, had a team of volunteers on stand-by to fly out to Kosovo. They were not required, but Major Alexander provided an expert manager for a four-day visit in July to examine the water distribution system. Major Roger Robinson, of Tarmac, now Carillion, was also on stand-by to give advice on quarrying but was not required.

For the Royal Logistic Corps the Kosovo operation was equally complicated and brought similar surprises. An extract from the citation for the Staff Corps Prize in 2000 awarded to Captain Gillian Jenkins for her work the previous year illustrates one of the early problems.

> She [Captain Jenkins] was responsible for the supply of food for the whole British force in Macedonia, Albania and Kosovo.... At virtually no notice in April she was tasked to provide food for over 50,000 Kosovar refugees who flooded into refugee camps in Macedonia to escape the atrocities in their own country.... Her quick action and total dedication in arranging this helped to save many lives.

For both troops and for the supply chain the most direct route to Kosovo was through the Greek port of Thessaloniki and up the only functioning rail link into Macedonia and on to Kosovo. This was also the only route that could carry heavy equipment and freight. Like the power supply the railway had been operated by Serbs, most of whom had disappeared; again like the power network the railway had been very poorly maintained. In addition the port workers at Thessaloniki were on strike, so the RLC found itself involved in operating a port as well as running a railway. Four locomotives had to be shipped in to keep the vast amount of freight moving. The RLC asked the Staff Corps for advice on locomotive maintenance – this was the first request ever received by the transport or logistic side of the Staff Corps for operational assistance.

Chapter Twelve

Conclusion

The requirement for secrecy in the work the Staff Corps undertook for the Army became obvious very early in its existence. In November 1866, when making a presentation on the solution to Exercise One, all the officers of the Corps were informed that any communication between the Staff Corps and the War Office was to be considered strictly confidential. It becomes even clearer how sensitive the engineer deliberations were considered when one notes that, with only one exception, no report from the engineer group concerned with the Exercises was ever allowed to be printed. Such secrecy about the Corps had obvious advantages for a Department of State and the Army but had the unfortunate consequence for the Staff Corps that very few people knew of its existence or its work on behalf of the nation. The numerous proposals throughout its history that the Staff Corps should be disbanded can all be attributed to ignorance of the Staff Corps, its role and its work. It is hoped that this short history will play some part in leading to a better understanding of a unique component of the British Army.

The original concept of the Staff Corps and its role in support of the Army in the defence of the homeland has not been relevant since the late 19th century. In both World Wars the nation found other ways of engaging the talents of professionals in the engineering and transport industries. The total lack of involvement of the Staff Corps in any major operation before 1980 suggests that when the United Kingdom had a large army to deploy the Staff Corps' services were not required.

The Army has changed out of all recognition since the date of the Staff Corps' foundation in 1865, when officers could obtain their commissions by purchase, flogging was still a widespread punishment, and the conditions of service and training of soldiers were given scant attention. The Staff Corps has responded to all the changes in the Army quietly and efficiently. As well as the concept, the method of working and the title of the Staff Corps have changed too; the only thing that has not is the conditions of service. It is still a body of unpaid volunteers, all highly professional individuals, available to give advice and assistance to the Army whenever called upon. The present roles of supporting both the Royal Engineers and the Royal Logistic Corps, in training, planning and operations, fit easily and happily together.

As the size of the Armed Forces has been progressively reduced during the last 30 years and the training of engineer and logistic specialists has been curtailed for financial and manpower reasons, the calls upon the Staff Corps have increased greatly. There is now much more emphasis on joint operations in the Armed Forces, the tasks being given to them seem to be getting broader, and they are being deployed into areas unknown or unfamiliar to them. It is reasonable to conclude that the role of the Staff Corps can only increase under these influences. The Staff Corps can respond with great speed when required, as it did in 1999 when an advisor was mobilised in the UK and was on the spot in Kosovo 48 hours later over a weekend.

The only three major operations of recent years have all involved the Staff Corps and they illustrate well the different kinds of help that can be given. Operation Corporate in the Falklands called for sophisticated and highly technical professional advice, sometimes on the ground, for soldiers to carry out unfamiliar engineering work to bring an unexpected military operation to a successful conclusion. For Operation Granby in the Gulf, on the other hand, there was plenty of warning and therefore the Staff Corps was able to give advice, information and intelligence requested before the operations began. The tasks to be performed by both Engineer and Logistic troops were those trained for, but in unfamiliar terrain of which Staff Corps members had recent and more relevant experience. The tasks in the Republics of the former Yugoslavia for both Engineers and Logisticians were to a large extent civil practice done in a civil environment where civil authority and capability were absent. Again, as in the Falklands, visits to the operational areas were involved.

Overlying all these periods of high activity is the constant advice and training given to the two Regular Corps. Seminars, lectures, recommendations on policy, reviewing military pamphlets and helping with officers' professional training seldom attract notice outside the two Regular Corps but are the essence of learning best practice so that the serving soldier can do the optimum job in the circumstances in which he finds himself.

It is the historian's task to draw lessons from past events not to prophesy, but the role of the Commanding Officer and the management of the Staff Corps may have a new duty in the future. As the British Armed Forces, and the Army in particular, become committed to operations which are not in defence of the realm, such as United Nations forces in foreign countries for humanitarian or political purposes, the potential for conflicts of interest can arise and there will be a need for the subject to be monitored in future.

It would not be appropriate to end this conclusion without a comment as to how the Staff Corps and its members see their role in the future.

As the events recounted in this history show there has been a steady increase in the number and variety of calls made on the resources of the Staff Corps and this seems more than likely to continue. The Commanding Officer and the members recognise that they will be required to react and respond to the changing needs of our military and political leaders as the Armed Services become more and more involved in world-wide events, yet with limited resources at their disposal.

Pro-active initiatives by the Staff Corps are largely confined to the two Liaison Groups, established by Colonel Ian Campbell 20 years ago. There can be no doubt that for both the Army and the Staff Corps they were an inspired innovation that not only opened up the full resources of the Staff Corps to the Services but also widened and eased the channels of communication. For the members of the Staff Corps involved the Liaison Groups continue to provide an opportunity to contribute to the work of the Royal Engineers and the Royal Logistic Corps; the various seminars arranged through them are welcomed as a stimulating challenge, rewarded by the enthusiastic reception they engender.

Even with the increase in the calls on the assistance of officers of the Staff Corps and the commercial pressures on senior engineers, logisticians and managers in industry, from whom the members are chosen to provide the expertise the Army requires to be available, there has been no difficulty in recruiting nor lack of willingness to respond when called, nor is any foreseen in the future.

The members of the Staff Corps are or soon become strong supporters of the two Regular Army Corps to which they respond and continue to stand ready to serve their interests and the national interest as circumstances dictate.

Key members of the Engineer and Logistic Staff Corps RE since its formation

The ranks, titles, names and decorations shown below are those applying at the time each person ceased serving the Staff Corps.

Honorary Colonels

1865–1894 General Sir W M S McMurdo, GCB

1894–1903 Field Marshal Sir John Simmons, GCB, GCMG

1903–1924 Major General D A Scott, CVO, CB, DSO, TD

1924–1948 Lieutenant General the Hon Sir Richard Montagu-Stuart-Wortley, KCB

1948–1961 Major General Sir Donald McMullen, KBE, CB, DSO

1961–1970 General the Lord Robertson of Oakridge, GCB, GBE, KCMG, DSO

1970–1977 General Sir Charles Jones, GCB, CBE, MC

1977–1983 General Sir William Jackson, GBE, KCB, MC and bar

1983–1988 Major General M E Tickell, CBE, MC

1988–1993 Major General G B Sinclair, CB, CBE

1993–2001 Major General J A J P Barr, CB, CBE

2001– Lieutenant General Sir Anthony Pigott, KCB, CBE

Lieutenant Colonels Commandant

1865–1878 Lieutenant Colonel G P Bidder

1878–1891 Lieutenant Colonel Sir John Hawkshaw, Kt.

1891–1898 Lieutenant Colonel Sir John Fowler, Bart., KCMG, VD

1898–1912 Lieutenant Colonel J C Hawkshaw, VD

1912–1914 Lieutenant Colonel R Elliot-Cooper, VD

1914–1920 Lieutenant Colonel Sir William Forbes, Kt., TD

1920–1924 Lieutenant Colonel C B D H Dent, TD

1924 Lieutenant Colonel Sir Maurice Fitzmaurice, Kt.

Officers Commanding

1924–1937 Colonel Sir Herbert Walker, KCB, TD

1937–1939 Colonel Sir Ralph Wedgwood, Bart., TD

1939–1941 Colonel the Lord Stamp, GCB, GBE

1941–1947 Colonel Sir James Milne, KCVO

1948–1949 Colonel Sir William Halcrow, Kt.

1949–1951 Colonel Sir Eustace Missenden, Kt.

1951–1956 Colonel V A M Robertson, CBE, MC

1956–1963 Colonel Sir John Elliot, Kt.

1963–1964 Colonel Sir Alexander Valentine, Kt.

1964–1969 Colonel G A Wilson, CBE

1969–1974 Colonel Sir Ralph Freeman, Kt., CVO, CBE

1974–1978 Colonel J R Hammond, MBE

1978–1981 Colonel Sir Kirby Laing, Kt.

1981–1986 Colonel I M Campbell, CVO

1986–1991 Colonel C T Wyatt

1991–1995 Colonel D J Lee, CBE

1995–1997 Colonel W Hogbin, CBE

1997–2001 Colonel J R Hennessy, OBE

2001– Colonel G O Whitehead, CBE

Acting Adjutants

1865–1884 Lieutenant Colonel C Manby

1884–1898 Lieutenant Colonel J C Hawkshaw, VD

1899–1902 Lieutenant Colonel A J Barry, CBE, TD

1902–1912 Lieutenant Colonel R Elliot-Cooper, VD

1912–1924 Lieutenant Colonel Sir Maurice Fitzmaurice, Kt.

1924–1938 Lieutenant Colonel Sir George Humphreys, Kt., TD

1938–1963 Lieutenant Colonel R D Gwyther, CBE, MC

1963–1982 Colonel D C Coode, CBE

1982–1993 Colonel J P Taberner, OBE

1994– Colonel R M Stancombe

Index

Photographic Acknowledgements

Photographs are supplied by or are reproduced courtesy of: © Crown copyright: pages 48-9;
© Crown copyright 2000, produced by Ministry of Defence: pages 80, 86; © Crown copyright, HQ
Engineer-in-Chief: pages 70, 71; Imperial War Museum: pages 51, 54, 58 (top); Institution of Civil Engineers:
pages 13, 16; Institution of Royal Engineers: front cover, pages 20, 26, 30, 31, 52 (bottom); Ministry of
Defence (all Crown copyright): Logistic Support Division, Headquarters Land Command, page 43; Air
Historical Branch, pages 44, 45, 52 (top); National Army Museum: page 19; National Railway Museum/Science
& Society Picture Library: page 37; Technical Information Centre, Royal Engineers: pages 46, 60 (both), 72, 77.
All other photographs are from private sources. Applications to reproduce the Crown copyright material in
this publication should be addressed to HMSO, The Copyright Unit, St Clements House, 2-16 Colegate,
Norwich NR3 1BQ; fax 01603 723000; email copyright@hmso.gov.uk